The Apothecaries 1617-1967

The Great Hall at Apothecaries' Hall

The
Worshipful
Society of

APOTHECARIES

of London

A HISTORY
1617-1967

Dr W. S. C. Copeman

PERGAMON PRESS

OXFORD · LONDON · EDINBURGH · NEW YORK
TORONTO · SYDNEY · PARIS · BRAUNSCHWEIG

Pergamon Press Ltd., Headington Hill Hall, Oxford
4 & 5 Fitzroy Square, London W.1
Pergamon Press (Scotland) Ltd., 2 & 3 Teviot Place Edinburgh 1
Pergamon Press Inc., 44–01 21st Street, Long Island City, New York 11101
Pergamon of Canada, Ltd., 5 Adelaide Street East, Toronto, Ontario
Pergamon Press (Aust.) Pty. Ltd., 20–22 Margaret Street,
Sydney, New South Wales
Pergamon Press S.A.R.L., 24 rue des Écoles, Paris 5e
Vieweg & Sohn GmbH, Burgplatz 1, Braunschweig

Edited and designed by
NEWMAN NEAME LTD
4 Fitzroy Square, London W1
A MEMBER OF THE PERGAMON GROUP
OF COMPANIES
and printed for them by
W & J Mackay & Co Ltd, Chatham, Kent
08 0037739

Contents

Illustrations

Cover Engraving: The Apothecaries' Prayer by Thomas Rowlandson, 1801
Frontispiece: The Great Hall at Apothecaries' Hall

Foreword

By HUGH SINCLAIR, L.M.S.S.A., D.M., F.R.C.P.
Master of the Society of Apothecaries, 1967–8

On December 6th, 1967, the Worshipful Society of Apothecaries of London met to celebrate the 350th anniversary of the first meeting after its Charter had been granted by James VI of Scotland and I of England. Such an anniversary afforded an opportunity to review the past, rejoice in the present and plan for the future. The Court of the Society arranged a week of celebration with a special Livery Dinner on the actual anniversary day at which Her Majesty Queen Elizabeth the Queen Mother graciously proposed the toast of the Society. Our Clerk and Registrar, Mr. Ernest Busby, also received the L.M.S.S.A. *honoris causa*. Subsequently she graciously accepted a copy of this Commemorative Volume.

In 1614 James VI and I accepted the advice of his Law Officers (one of whom was the great Sir Francis Bacon) to separate the Apothecaries from the Grocers, one of the twelve great City Livery Companies. The king decided: "Grocers are but merchants, the business of an Apothecary is a Mistery, wherefore I think it fitting that they be a Corporation of themselves."

The Society's evolution from this point is amply described in the book. Today it continues to grant a fully registrable medical qualification, the L.M.S.S.A., and in recent years it has been responsible for founding two post-graduate Diplomas, in Industrial Health and in Medical Jurisprudence, each the first of its kind. The Society also still grants a certificate of Dispensers, now known as Pharmacy Technicians. Eight years ago the Society founded its Faculty of the History of Medicine and Pharmacy, which is playing a most important part in stimulating this hitherto neglected subject in this country; three endowed annual lectures are given under its auspices; and the day after the Livery Dinner on December 6th, at a dinner for the members of the Society who are members of the Faculty, the Archbishop of Canterbury proposed its health. Earlier in the week at a soirée the Freedom of the Society by Gift was bestowed on the Faculty's Honorary Secretary, Dr. F. N. L. Poynter, and its Chairman, Dr. W. S. C. Copeman, delivered his Gideon De Laune Lecture, "In Praise of Apothecaries", upon which this excellent history is based. At the end of the week of celebration the Minister of Health was the principal guest at the Yeomanry Dinner.

This Commemorative Volume, apart from reviewing the past, illustrates the magnificent premises the Society occupies, worthy of any City Guild. Our Great Hall, the site of which has been in the possession of the Society since 1632 and which was rebuilt between 1668 and 1670, is the oldest surviving Hall of any City Livery Company and the oldest medical building still in use in the country.

We are indeed grateful to Dr. Copeman, to whom the Society has often been indebted, for this History. With this honourable past commemorated in it, the Society looks forward to the future, confident that it will continue to play an important part in the prevention and cure of disease.

Preface

This memorial volume is based upon the author's 1967 Gideon De Laune Lecture delivered as part of the celebrations by the Society to commemorate the 350th anniversary of the granting of its Royal Charter by King James I. It constitutes a brief historical record of the Society's life and activities, and is much indebted to the two main historical accounts which both deal with many of these matters in far greater detail. These are C. R. B. Barratt's History published for the Society in 1905, and Dr. E. A. Underwood's two volumes based largely upon the MSS. left by Dr. Cecil Wall and Dr. Hector Cameron (1963). The Society's Minute Books, kept since 1617, are complete and have been consulted. Sir Zachary Cope's Gideon De Laune lecture, which was published in the *British Medical Journal*, January 1956, has also proved of immense help regarding the Society's educational achievements. The Society's Clerk, Mr. Ernest Busby, has given great assistance. So have several members of the Court, notably Mr. Alistair Gunn, and Sir John Richardson, who has kindly read the proofs.

The Director of the Wellcome Medical Historical Museum and Library, Dr. Poynter, who is also the Honorary Secretary of the Society's Historical Faculty, has generously allowed his Director of the Department of Illustration, Mr. S. H. Watkins, to supply most of the illustrations. Miss A. Lothian, Librarian of the Pharmaceutical Society, kindly supplied that of the Apothecary's jar, whilst the Royal College of Physicians allowed me to reproduce for the first time its portrait of Sir Charles Dodds.

Lastly, but by no means least, it must be recorded that Mr. Robert Maxwell, M.C., M.P., generously offered to produce this volume and that his colleagues Mr. A. J. Budden and Mr. J. J. Greenwood gave copiously of their editorial time and expertise.

W. S. C. COPEMAN

From the Most High cometh healing. The Lord hath created Medicines out of the Earth: and he that is wise will not abhor them. Of such doth the Apothecary make a confection. He hath given men skill that he might be honoured in his marvellous works; and of his works there are no end . . . with such he doth heal a man and taketh away his pains.

There is a time when in their [Apothecaries'] hands there is good success, for they shall pray to the Lord that he prosper that which they give for curing and relief, and remedies to prolong life. So let him not go from thee, for thou hast need of him.

Ecclesiasticus, Chapter XXXVIII
Part of the Lesson read on Master's Day

IACOBVS D.G. MAGNÆ BRITANNIÆ FRANCIÆ ET HIBERNIÆ REX.

· En tibi, Rex, suprâ, cum Pallade doctus Apollo,
  In laudes meritò, Magne Iacobe, tuas:
Infrâ te posita est Pax alma et Copia rerum,
  Quam felix populus, Magne Iacobe, tuus?

C. G. fecit:

And are to be sold in Lombard
streets by Iohn Bofwel.

James I of England, James VI of Scotland.

I

James I gives a Royal Charter

THE ANCIENT CITY COMPANIES OF London arose in medieval times as "Friendly Societies", usually among the congregation of certain churches. Their object was primarily mutual help and the support of distressed colleagues. Gradually their membership tended to become the prerogative of certain trades or guilds which in time they came to control. Their privileges were eventually established by Royal Charter. So these City Companies became powerful and rich and their Freemen would elect each year a Lord Mayor, Sheriffs and Aldermen as guardians of their civic privileges. Their religious origin is today still remembered by attendance at the appropriate City church to hear a sermon preached on Master's Day. The Apothecaries' special church is St. Andrew's-by-the-Wardrobe. As will be shown, the evolution of our Company is unique in that as a craft guild fulfilling its original functions it has evolved into its present status of a professional licensing body. The London apothecary, from a lowly Elizabethan compounder of drugs, has become a fully qualified medical practitioner, recognised by the State. The history of this metamorphosis is interesting and important, and we must begin at the beginning.

In Shakespeare's time, when our Society started, there were no general practitioners of medicine. There were only physicians, who were learned, scarce and expensive, surgeons who were unlettered craftsmen, and quacks of all sorts, some of them very picturesque but probably dangerous people. Until the dissolution of the monasteries the monks had also played a part in caring for the sick and poor, and it may have seemed significant to our founders that their Hall had once been the Hospice of the Black Friars, who for three centuries had supplied these needs of the City. The London of 1617 was still in appearance a medieval City confined within walls, whose streets were dark and narrow and the houses half-timbered. It was dominated by the towering pile of St. Paul's. London's highway was the Thames. The merchants of the City all lived over their place of business, each particular trade tending to cluster in the same region. Most of the apothecary trade was carried out around "sweet-smelling" Bucklesbury.

The evolution of the medical profession

Throughout history the priest-physician had been the embodiment of medical learning; he was an academic who tended to live in an intellectual "Ivory Tower", but was employed professionally by the rich and powerful. In 1518 the Physicians were Incorporated by Henry VIII as a College, un-shackled by the Church and given the privilege of licensing practitioners, and so remained all-powerful rulers of the profession for another three centuries. The surgeons, however skilled, worked only to the physician's direction and were considered as craftsmen of lowly status. In 1540 they, too, had become incorporated, with their "brothers of the knife", the barbers, and accepted custom subsequently allowed them some degree of independence in the treatment of external injuries and complaints. This was basically the situation in 1617, when the Apothecaries obtained their Charter, which freed them from membership of the Grocers' Company.

Every royal palace and great household from time immemorial had had an official known at various times as the Spicer or the Pepperer, but later as the *Apothecarius*, whose task was to administer the precious stores of drugs, spices, perfumes and sweetmeats. In time of sickness the physician would direct him to produce and apply the former, so he soon developed some tradition of medical practice on a lowly executive plane. The office of the Court Apothecary has an unbroken history from the reign of King John to the present day. These men, looking for a trade guild in which their interests could be centralised, joined "the craft and mistery of the Company of

Grocers", which imported and sold the drugs, spices and medicinal compounds with which they worked. The term mistery (or mystery) in this sense implies a collection of masters of the same craft entrusted with powers for its regulation. The grocer-apothecary, however, remained a somewhat specialised member of that Company, concerning himself with the retailing and compounding of drugs and medicines, as opposed to his colleagues' activities in the wholesale importation and retailing of groceries and culinary spices. Moreover the development of overseas trade and the consequent increased prosperity of the City made it possible to compound medicines which had previously had to be imported, and so some degree of special technical training and expertise had developed as early as the reign of Henry VI.

These apothecaries increasingly began to feel the need for a corporation of their own. As early as 1525 they were officially referred to as though a separate and distinct body and were granted certain privileges and

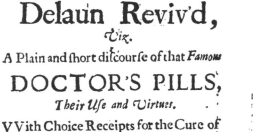

An 18th century advertisement for De Laune's pills.

restrictions in contemporary Bills and Charters. These included the Act of
1523 whereby Henry VIII confirmed the Charter of the College of Physicians
and decreed that "th' apothecaryes maye be swore and uppon a payne com-
maunded that they shall not serve any byll (prescription) of any physicians
not examyned and approved by the College". In a further Act of 1540 their
work was recognised for the first time as a specialised "mistery" and the
"Wardens of the said mystery of Apothecaries within the said city" were
excused certain civic duties, and were given the right, jointly with the
Censors of the College of Physicians, to search retail apothecaries' shops in
and around the City and destroy faulty wares.

In 1588 they unsuccessfully petitioned Queen Elizabeth for a monopoly
of compounding and selling drugs and medicines, being worried by the news
that the College had itself rented a Physic Garden and appointed the famous
herborist John Gerard as its Curator. In 1607 the Charter of the Grocers'
Company was amended in such a way that the Apothecaries were to be
recognised as a separate section of that Company, but as this did not give
them representation upon the Court the majority of them shortly endea-
voured under the leadership of Dr. Gideon De Laune, Anne of Denmark's
Apothecary, to promote a separatist Bill in Parliament. It became increasingly obvious, however, that secession was imminent and that a new profession, pharmacy, involving special training and close study, was evolving.

The Charter

So in 1614 De Laune and the Apothecaries petitioned the King direct for a
charter, such as had been granted to the College of Physicians and also to
the Barber-Surgeons, for the following reasons: "Very many Empiricks and
unskillful and ignorant men do abide in the City of London . . . which are
not well instructed in the Art or Mystery of Apothecaries, but do make and
compound many unwholesome, hurtful, dangerous and corrupt medicines
and the same do sell . . . to the great peril and daily hazard of the lives of
the King's subjects." Sir Francis Bacon, as Chief Law Officer, was consulted,
and having no love for physicians saw that he could cause them great
annoyance by supporting the cause of the Apothecaries. His Committee
therefore reported that the Art of the Apothecaries was a separate one, and
should not be subordinated to fallible merchants and tradesmen like the
Grocers, who favoured only the lucrative part of their trade.

The King accepted this advice, saying: "Grocers are but merchants, the business of an Apothecary is a Mistery, wherefore I think it fitting that they be a Corporation of themselves." But as this naturally displeased the powerful City Fathers things did not progress smoothly. The position became further complicated by the presence of a minority of apothecary-grocers who still preferred the flesh-pots and the comfortable status of membership of the Grocers', second only in rank among the twelve great Companies of the City. They had no desire to be led into the wilderness, so these men petitioned their Prime Warden to discipline the seceders, whom they unscrupulously described as "tobacco sellers" in order to prejudice them in the eyes of King James, whose dislike for that herb was well known. The apothecarial rebels, however, eventually carried conviction at Court by the plea that their art concerned the life and health of the people and so put them into a unique position among the other City Companies whose sole interest was with commerce. They were able, moreover, to cite the precedent of separate incorporation of apothecaries in every other great city in Christendom. With incautious *naïveté* which they were to regret for the next two centuries they suggested that they should put their dependence upon and work with the liberal-minded and noble physicians who then resided in the City, who would undoubtedly be more sympathetic to their aims than the mercenary grocers.

The King was suitably impressed, and on the advice of his physician, Sir Theodore de Mayerne, he ordered that a Charter should be drawn up immediately. This was done on April 24, 1615. But, like Pharaoh of old, the Grocers' Company still refused to let the children go and was able to hinder their exodus until December 6, 1617, on which day it passed the Great Seal. The first entry in our Minute Book reads: "The 16th of December 1617: The Master, Wardens and Assistants hereafter named took their oaths at Grays' Inn before Mr. Attorney-General, Mr. Dr. Atkins, and Mr. Dr. Mayerne, the King's Physician, being hereunto authorised under the Great Seale of England."

The new Court of Assistants met for the first time nine days later, independent at last, with little money and no home, but with boundless confidence in their future. Their written records have survived intact from that day. The real hero of the campaign, Gideon De Laune, who was the son of a refugee French Protestant pastor practising medicine in London, was still

19

technically a foreigner and so remained ineligible for the Mastership of his new Company until 1628, but the influence at Court which he was able to exert and his generous benefactions render it fitting that he should be regarded as the principal founder of the Company or Society of Apothecaries.

It is noteworthy that in the Charter the term "Society" is used, although it was not until almost a century later that it supplanted the usual civic nomenclature of "Company" in general usage. By the final wording of their Charter the Apothecaries had managed to avoid that official subjection to the Physicians which they had feared inevitable, and for this favour Lord Chancellor Bacon was presented by them with "a Taster of gold, worth between forty and fifty pounds, and a present of rare Ambergrease".

After this stormy start, although now reasonably secure through the possession of a Charter, the new Company continued to suffer the hostility of the City, led by the Grocers. However, so long as Bacon still enjoyed power and while the King lived all went well. But with the death of James the claims of the College of Physicians to dominate them were revived. The main matter of dispute by this time was the fact that the Apothecaries were coming to be regarded as the general medical attendants of the sick poor. This position had been forced upon them by the large numbers of sufferers "unable or unwilling to fee a leech or a physician" who sought their aid. They recognised that they had no legal right to claim a fee for their advice and services, but found adequate remuneration through their charges for dispensing the remedies they advised.

The new Company itself officially regarded its main function as being to improve the quality of all drugs sold to His Majesty's subjects, and also to better the qualifications of the vendors. It was inevitable, however, that the individual apothecary should gradually develop from a mere dispenser of other people's prescriptions into one who included a little professional advice with the package, and so eventually into a general practitioner of medicine, who thus infringed the College's monopoly of medical practice within the City and for seven miles around. This situation spread gradually throughout the country, as we shall see, the apothecary practising at first from his shop in the local city or town and later throughout the countryside.

The constitution of the new Society followed the plan usual among City Companies, then as now. After serving his apprenticeship a member would become a Yeoman or Journeyman once his application for the Freedom of

Sir Theodore Turquet de Mayerne (1573–1655)
Physician to James I.

the City had been granted and the appropriate fees paid. Later he would be promoted to the Livery and so acquire the full rights of a Free Citizen of London, including the privilege of voting at the annual election for the Lord Mayor and his Sheriffs on Midsummer's Day. Eventually he might be elected to the Court of Assistants, ultimately serving as Warden and Master.

II

A Hall
is Built
and
Burnt

A FEW INFLUENTIAL APOTHECARIES such as Gideon De Laune were still engaged in lucrative wholesale trade in drugs on a large scale, and for them there was little temptation to practise medicine. It was such men who two hundred years later were to break away from the Apothecaries' Company, which had by then become predominantly medical, and found the Pharmaceutical Society. Yet others were attracted to the more scientific aspects of botany and materia medica and later of pharmacy and pharmacology.

Most apothecaries at that time were comparatively obscure people and seldom "hit the headlines", as we should say now. So it is of interest to note the apprenticeship in 1634 to Stephen Higgins, the aged Master of the Company, of the notorious Nicholas Culpepper (1615–54), an anti-Establishment figure who after serving in the Parliamentary army and being wounded at the battle of Newbury decided to set up as a "physician and astrologer" in Spitalfields without further qualification. He translated the College Pharmacopoeia into the vernacular, incorporating some scurrilous comments on both the College and those Fellows of whom he disapproved, thereby infuriating the Physicians, who referred to it as being done "very filthily by two years' drunken labour . . . corrupting men's minds with his

*A medical consultation and an Apothecary's shop,
17th century.*

opinions besides the danger of poysoning men's bodies". But new editions of this and his other works continued to appear for over a century, and the proceeds afforded the chief financial support of his widow. A copy was recently sold at Sotheby's for £1,000. He became well known during his short life as the result of royalist persecution and also his specious thesis regarding the affinities between medical herbs and certain phases of the planets, and his professed concern for the poor. He has re-achieved fame in our time in the pages of Kipling's *Puck of Pook's Hill*. His book was a pioneer of the popular "self-help" medical type. For instance, a useful prescription for bed-wetting is as follows: "burn a white mouse to a powder, and give it in new milk. This will cure this disease." There are very many others equally helpful.

The average small apothecary's shop of that period was probably not a very impressive or hygienic place. It may not have been quite so bad, however, as the one described by Garth, an enemy of apothecaries. In his poem *The Dispensary* he writes:

> Aloft in rows large poppy-heads were strung
> And near, a scaly alligator hung.
> In this place drugs in musty heaps decayed,
> In that dried bladders and false teeth were laid.

The hostility both of the College of Physicians and the City authorities towards the Apothecaries flared up again towards the middle of the seventeenth century and they obtained an Order in Council ordaining amongst other limitations that "no apothecary is to sell any poyson drugge or medecine" except on prescription by a physician. The indignant apothecaries suggested with some justice that if to prevent danger apothecaries must not sell poisonous drugs then the cutlers should be forbidden to sell knives and gun-makers pistols. They also took the opportunity of jibing at "the willinge absence of the Physicians" during the recent plague which had compelled the Apothecaries to take over the care of the health of the King's subjects. As the matter seems to have progressed no further, we may perhaps assume that the Attorney-General, who was in charge of the Order, must have been impressed by these counter-arguments. This annoyed the Physicians still further and they proposed accordingly only to employ those apothecaries who would acknowledge their subservient status, hoping that

In Effigiem. Nicholai Culpeper Equitis .

The shaddow of that Body heer you find
Which serves but as a case to hold his mind;
His Intellectuall part be pleas'd to looke
In lively lines described in the Booke . *Crofs sculp: it*

Nicholas Culpeper (1616–54).

the others would eventually comply with their demands or else be forced to abandon their business owing to lack of trade.

The dispute continued with increasing acrimony, which culminated in the committal by the President of the College of three or four apothecaries to Newgate Gaol for malpractice. The Keeper of Newgate, however, owing to some error, set them at liberty, whereupon their leader George Hamilton sued the College Censors for false imprisonment. This resulted in an agreement by the Privy Council at the request of the College to look into the validity of the Apothecaries' Charter, an action which filled the latter with alarm, as it posed a direct threat to their continued corporate existence.

Subscriptions were invited towards a defence fund, but as the response proved far from unanimous a policy of appeasement was decided on by the Court of the Society. The Master, Josiah Harris, together with his two Wardens, waited upon the President "to know what the College of Physicians would desire of this Company". The Physicians must have given them a clear-cut answer, for on September 23, 1635, a document signed by the Master and most of the Court was delivered which satisfied the College. In this the signatories expressed their desire "to bringe ourselves againe into the goode opinion of the College of Physicians uppon whome wee doe depend".

The bigwigs of the City, however, were not to be appeased so easily, and they petitioned the King to revoke the Apothecaries' Charter. But the Stuarts, whatever their failings, were generally anxious to be on the side of science. King James himself came to the City and told the Court of Aldermen that he gave this Charter from his own judgement for the health of the people, "knowing that Grocers are not competent judges of the practice of Medicine". So the Company was saved, and later in the year they diplomatically presented the Lord Mayor with a tun of wine. The following year they were invited to join his procession.

During the Civil War the Apothecaries, like most other City Companies, supported the Parliamentary cause and were subjected to considerable taxes in support of its New Model Army. In 1645 some of Cromwell's troops, after their triumphant entry into London under their commander Sir Thomas Fairfax, were quartered in the Hall, and the damage they did put the Company to great expense. Shortly afterwards the Apothecaries were "privileged" to entertain the Lord Protector himself, together with numerous civic guests, an enterprise which they found neither cheap nor rewarding.

Individual apothecaries, however, seem to have done very well as the result of supplying the Commonwealth medical necessities. Parliament ordered the Master and Wardens to find medical officers for its force amongst members of the Company, but there exists no evidence that they ever did so.

In 1685 James II came to the throne with political powers undreamed of

Title page of the Pharmaco-poeia Londinensis (1618) of the Royal College of Physicians.

by his immediate predecessors. In order to establish his influence firmly in the City he revoked the Charters of all the Companies, including the Apothecaries'. Thus they became unwillingly political machines of the Court until as the result of the revolution three years later William and Mary succeeded James, and all the original charters and privileges were restored. Upon this happy note of amicable co-operation with the City and the College, precarious as it sometimes proved, we can turn to the material environment of the Apothecaries, particularly their Hall, of which they were becoming justifiably proud.

The Great Hall

When the Apothecaries left the Grocers' Company they were without a hall of their own, although they expressed a determined desire to build one which should be fully worthy of the status to which they aspired. They had no accumulated funds, however, and their minimum annual expenditure exceeded their income. It was not until 1631 that they were at last out of debt and found themselves a suitable property in fashionable Blackfriars comprising ¾ acre, the site of the Dominican monastery, just within the old City Wall in the angle between the Thames and its noisome tributary the River Fleet, which still flows, imprisoned within an iron pipe, under Bridge Street into the Thames.

On November 17, 1632, an agreement was reached with the owner of Cobham House, Anne, Lady Howard of Effingham, and the Company with the assistance of De Laune acquired the house and some more surrounding land,* which included the Blackfriars Theatre in Playhouse Yard, of which William Shakespeare had been a shareholder and where several of his plays had had their first nights. They paid £1,800 in two instalments. On December 11 a meeting of the whole Company was held there amidst great rejoicing. Gradually furnishings and ornaments for the new Hall were contributed or purchased, and by the time of the Fire of 1666 the Company's inventory shows that they owned a considerable quantity of ornamental gold- and silverware in addition to much handsome furniture and portraits.

The Great Fire

It was early in the morning of Sunday, September 2, 1666, that the Great

* Dr. F. N. L. Poynter has recently tracked down the original title-deeds and generously presented them to the Society.

Fire of London broke out in Pudding Lane, although it did not reach Blackfriars until Tuesday. It proved impossible, however, to preserve many of the Society's possessions, although luckily the Charter and records were salved from the burning Hall. The portrait of Gideon De Laune attributed to Cornelius Janssen which had been presented in 1642 was missing until it found its way back, more than a century later, and was hung in the Court Room, where it still presides, showing evidence of slight charring (*opp. p.* 32). Following the disaster of the Great Fire the Apothecaries displayed enormous energy. Within a very few years their Hall had been rebuilt and refurnished with help from Sir Christopher Wren's chief assistant, and their land rehabilitated. With the smell of fire still in their nostrils they inserted a clause in all their building leases that no follower of such inflammatory trades as blacksmiths or tallow chandlers should ever be eligible as tenants. The only reference to this disaster in the Court Minutes, however, is to "the recent conflagration"!

The work of rebuilding was begun in April 1668. The Great Hall reproduced the features of its predecessor, including the lack of provision for heating. It seems probable that a central brazier was used and that the smoke escaped through a louvre in the roof. The work of panelling the Court Room was completed in 1671 by subscription, and still remains unaltered. Shortly afterwards Dr. William Croone, an original Fellow of the Royal Society and the son-in-law of John Lorrimer, Master and Benefactor of the Apothecaries' Company, visited the Hall and offered to decorate the Parlour in his memory. Lorrimer's armorial bearings were to be placed in the window, and the fireplace tiled with marble. It is sad to record that Croone seems not to have fulfilled his fine promises, as five years later the Company had to make substantial payment for this purpose. He was founder of the lectures at the Royal College of Physicians which bear his name.

New furniture was soon acquired, which included the six tables still in use in the Hall, made of that recently introduced hardwood, mahogany. There is also much mention throughout the records of the large numbers of silver spoons possessed by the Company. These resulted from the custom by which every apprentice who completed his Articles should present a gilt or silver spoon on taking the Oath. The Company, when in need of small extra sums of money, was in the habit of selling parcels of these by

The Apothecaries' Hall, c. 1800.

weight. Only one example remains with us, so perhaps the custom should be revived!

The fine bust of Gideon De Laune, which stands on the screen executed by the King's Master Carver in the Great Hall, was completed in 1676 by Nicholas Young, a talented stonemason, in lieu of paying rent which he owed the Company. It is also interesting to remember that the handsome well which stands in the centre of the paved Courtyard outside the Great Hall is the one which provided the water supply of the Dominican monks in the thirteenth century; it still contains water.

Civic privileges

The distinction of wearing a special livery was grudgingly conferred by the Court of Aldermen of the City in 1630, after a long period of dispute regarding the ranking of the new Company within the civic hierarchy. By his Charter every Liveryman already possessed the right to take two paying

31

apprentices, and also to vote in the election for Aldermen and Lord Mayor on Midsummer's Day. From the middle of the eighteenth century Liverymen of the Apothecaries' Company acquired in addition the unique privilege of forming and purchasing shares in what was known as their "Navy Stock". This joint stock company resulted from the monopoly granted by Queen Anne to their laboratory to supply the medicinal requirements of her Royal Navy, and the dividends from this proved very profitable. It is said that it was owing to the need to direct this venture, together with its rather less exclusive subsidiary the "Laboratory Stock" which manufactured pure drugs for general sale, that the Company seldom lacked good men of business to guide their affairs, and to repel the attacks of the envious Physicians. It was only in 1922 that the laboratory finally ceased to manufacture fine drugs, and that the shop situated on the north side of the courtyard from which they were retailed was merged into the present Main Hall.

For these reasons although the cost of accepting call to the Livery was high it was seldom refused. The ceremonial clothing with the Livery and hood was performed by the Master four times a year and was followed with "a greate Dynner, according to the auntyent Custome of the City", after which the members of the Company would repair to one of the neighbouring churches to hear a special sermon preached. Later the attendance at church of all Liverymen was enjoined only once annually on Master's Feast Day, when he was installed.

The Coat of Arms

It is probable that the original Livery gown worn by members of the Society was blue with yellow satin facings, similar to that still worn by the Bedel, the colours being derived from the Society's Grant of Arms. This was awarded by William Camden, Clarenceux King of Arms, only six days after the Charter had been sealed. The Arms of the Society depict Apollo, god of healing, overcoming the dragon of disease. The crest is a rhinoceros, whose powdered horn provided one of the chief contemporary "wonder drugs" retailed by the apothecary. The supporters are unicorns, King James's "special beast", which he introduced into the Royal Arms, and which indicate his personal interest in the Society's incorporation. The motto is *Opiferque Per Orbem Dicor*, which should be translated "I am

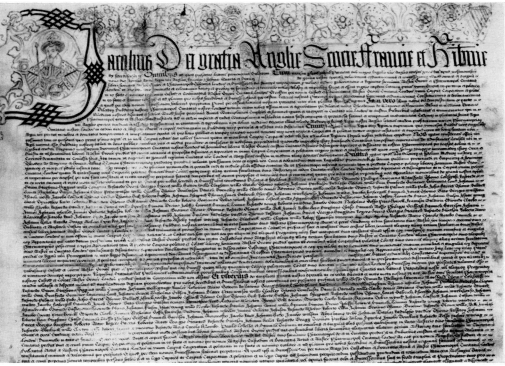

The Apothecaries Charter granted by James I.

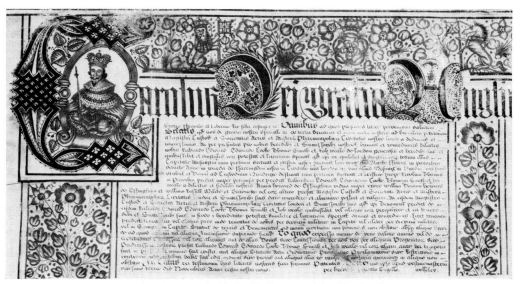

The licence to hold the Hall, granted by Charles I.

*Gideon De Laune (1565–1635) Apothecary to James I
and reputed founder of the Society of Apothecaries. The
painting in Apothecaries' Hall.*

Anne of Denmark (1574–1619) Queen of James I.
From a print by J. Houbraken.

Francis Bacon (1561–1626). A line-engraving by
J. Houbraken.

spoken of all over the world as one who brings help".*

It may have been in response to the sight of the Apothecaries proudly flaunting their new Livery in the streets of the City that the College of Physicians in the same year issued an order that all their Fellows, Members and Licentiates should wear their gowns when they went about the streets. Towards the end of the century, however, gowns had become purely ceremonial clothing and were donned only on special occasions. One such occasion was the annual Installation of a Master.

Masters' Day

This would begin at noon, when all Freemen of the Company would breakfast together in the library gallery "off a tremendous sirloin of beef". An hour later the first procession was formed to conduct the Master to church. The order was as follows:

The Band of Musick, Barge-Master with Coat and Badge, Bedel cloathed, with his Mace, the Stewards with their wands, the Clergymen, Preacher and Reader, the Master cloathed, the Upper and Renter Wardens, cloathed, members of the Court, by seniority, cloathed, Livery, also cloathed, and the Clerk.

After the service the procession returned in the same order, some alms being thrown to the poor *en route*. At the gateway they were met by another band and the stewards, who led them through the Great Hall into the Court Room, where the master called his Lady and led her back into the Hall for dinner, "which ought to be at half an hour after three". The Wardens then led their Ladies and took their seats on either side of the Master with their Ladies opposite. Next the Minister, who preached "with such Lady as the Master appoints" for his partner. After that all took their seats by seniority led by Past Masters, each with his Lady opposite. Dinner was punctuated with liberal toasts and lasted until five o'clock, when several new processions were formed, which in turn "perambulated the Hall". The old Master then with much ceremony resigned his place of honour and his successor, simulating great unwillingness at having so great an honour thrust upon him, was discovered in his scheduled hiding-place, "cloathed,

* It is said that in 1815, when the Society was entrusted with the control of all medical practice, there was a proposal to change the motto to *Auxilium ferimus iam nos medicantibus illis Majorem*, which roughly means: "We can now offer even greater help to the medical profession."

and a coronet placed upon his head". His health was then heartily drunk and the Band of Musick led the Company out into the Court Room, where the necessary new Oaths were administered and thanks duly paid. It appears from the records that the butler employed by the Company at many of these feasts was a woman, as was their plumber!

Then there was the *State Barge*, with a curtained room like the cabin of a gondola, which contained a raised seat for the Master covered with crimson silk damask and a foot-rest, with a crew of eighteen Lusty Watermen, with three banners showing the King's Arms, the City Arms and the Arms of the Company. This impressive equipage joined the procession on Lord Mayor's Day, and normally also conveyed the Master and his Court of Assistants to and from inspections of their Physic Garden at Chelsea. The remains of the Barge House can be seen in its south-east corner today. The last great Barge unaccountably sank in 1816 and was never replaced. Its last official function had been to take part "next before the Painter-Stainers" in the river cortège which had escorted the body of Lord Nelson to its resting-place in St. Paul's ten years previously. Its pennants and banners can be seen in the Great Hall today. The barge had also often been used for the Society's herbarising expeditions which took place at regular intervals. These pleasant functions consisted of organised outings to the countryside surrounding London on certain days of the year, to enable the apprentices to learn to recognise the simples and herbs from which most of their medicaments were prepared. These educational exercises were rounded off with dinner in the Society's Hall, and it is recorded that is was sometimes found difficult to maintain discipline and good manners on these occasions.

The chemical laboratories

The Society had established a laboratory for the compounding of vegetable (Galenic) medicines and for the instruction of their apprentices as early as 1623. They now added to this another for use with the new chemical substances which were coming into use, as late evidence of the practical direction to which alchemy had ultimately been turned (1671). This was a venture of great interest, as it was one of the first chemical laboratories to be established in this country. As the result of these "subsidiaries" it became possible for the first time to guarantee the purity of commercially produced drugs and to reduce their cost by mass-production. Thus the valuable monopoly already mentioned of supplying not only the Navy but later also the East India Company, the Army and the Crown Colonies was awarded to the Company and lasted until the mid-nineteenth century, bringing considerable wealth to top apothecaries, as well as some to their Company.

For long after the Great Fire the College of the suddenly impoverished Physicians lay in ruins at Amen Corner, so the Apothecaries' influence and status took a step forward. One thing, however, the Society lacked: a garden where they could grow those plants which could no longer be found flourishing in the fields, woods and commons of England, as well as those more exotic plants which were being increasingly described and imported from the New World and the East. The chief reason for the study of plants at that time was to discover and use their medicinal qualities. A Physic Garden therefore seemed to the progressive members of the Court very necessary, not only for the honour and dignity of the Society, but for the education proper to their apprentices, and as a source of raw materials for the laboratories. Some members of the Company who had no wish to practise medicine, like the famous Royal Herbalists James Parkinson and John Gerard (or Gerarde), were thus able to devote much of their lives to the scientific study of botany as an end in itself, or to horticulture, or to the writing of up-to-date herbals or textbooks of *materia medica*. Later, some founded great commercial drug houses in the City such as Allen and Hanbury, John Bell and Croyden, and Savory and Moore, which have prospered until the present day. Indeed, it was not until Lloyd George's Insurance Act of 1911 had increased the demand for pharmaceuticals so enormously that the Society's laboratory could no longer cope that the large commercial pharmaceutical firms finally took over. So in 1922, after three hundred years of pharmaceutical practice, the Apothecaries finally abandoned trade and became the purely professional body which it is today.

Statue of Sir Hans Sloane (1660–1753),
still standing in the Physic Garden.

III

The Chelsea Physic Garden

It WAS FOR SUCH REASONS AS those mentioned in the previous chapter that the Society rented four acres on the Chelsea waterside in 1673 from Lord Cheyne. A gardener was appointed and plants were transferred from the Westminster Herb Garden of William Gape, a Past-Master. Three years later a wall was built round it which still stands, and flanking the river gate they exultingly planted four cedars of Lebanon, then three feet high, the first ever to be grown in this country. The last of these monsters survived the deteriorating conditions of London air until 1904, and the chairs now used by the Master and Wardens are made from their wood. The Society was lucky in its appointment of John Watts as gardener in 1675, as he was generally considered a botanical genius. It may have been he who initiated the English greenhouse, for John Evelyn, himself no mean authority on gardening, recorded after one of many visits in 1685 that the "artifices used by Mr. Watts have been very effectual for the preservation of his plants, in so much that this severe winter has scarce kill'd any of his fine plants" owing to the "very ingenius subterranean heat conveyed by a stove under the Conserveatory . . . so as he leaves the doores and windowes open in the hardest frost".

It must have been a pleasant quiet place. Lord Clarendon, while awaiting

37

committal to the Tower for nonconformity in James II's reign, wrote that on several occasions he was in the Apothecaries' Garden at Chelsea, where he was never disturbed by any company, and where alone he could find peace. Watts's unbusinesslike habits, however, gradually became a serious liability to the Company, and in spite of subscriptions from members and others things went from bad to worse. Lord Cheyne offered them the freehold for £400, but the cash at their disposal could no longer even pay for repairs needed to save their State Barge. In 1714 it was reluctantly decided that the garden must be sold. Before doing so, however, they agreed to approach their new ground landlord, Sir Hans Sloane, for advice. This proved to be the great event in the history of the garden, bringing it new life.

Sir Hans, a rich and famous physician, who had enjoyed the unique distinction of Presidency both of his own College and of the Royal Society, and was also Physician both to Queen Anne and George I, had recently bought and retired to the ancient Manor of Chelsea. As a young medical student he had qualified at the Apothecaries' Hall and studied in the garden and grown to love it. So when approached he was inclined to help them, "for the manifestation of the power, wisdom and glory of God in the works of his creation and to show (the apprentices) how useful plants may be distinguished from those that be hurtful". As a good businessman, however, he wished for some guarantee that the needy Society would continue to maintain the garden permanently, so he imposed conditions: every year fifty specimens of plants all grown in the garden were to be presented to the Royal Society until at least 2,000 varieties had been achieved. In return he granted a lease in perpetuity (1722) for a nominal rent of £5 per annum. If the Society failed in this trust, the garden was to be offered firstly to the Royal Society, and if they declined to the Royal College of Physicians. If they both refused, it was to revert to his own heirs. His elder daughter married Lord Cadogan, whose descendant is therefore the present owner, and sits on its committee, although the garden flourishes now under the patronage of a Charitable Trust. It is said that in naming Sloane Street after Sir Hans the inhabitants of Chelsea symbolised his life in that it is very long, obviously prosperous and perfectly straight. His great collection of "natural objects" and books formed the nucleus of the British Museum after his death at the age of 93. He was the first medical man to receive the honour of a baronetcy.

Another service Sir Hans rendered the Society was to introduce the celebrated gardener and botanist Philip Miller, later F.R.S. (1691–1771), who was the first to suggest the part played by insects in the fertilisation of plants and was the author of *The Gardener's Dictionary* and other popular works. He devoted himself to the introduction and acclimatisation of rare plants from abroad by establishing correspondence with famous gardeners in all quarters of the globe, a practice which still continues. The great Linnaeus, the father of systematic botany, visited England to meet him and see the garden and, although they quarrelled, he laid out the garden anew on the Linnaean system in his honour. It was Philip Miller also who at the request of the Society sent out the first cotton seeds to the Governor of King George's new Colony for poor debtors called Georgia (1732), thinking that it might acclimatise well and afford their struggling economy some assistance. The content of this fateful packet was the parent of the cotton crops of the U.S. These in turn were the reason for the import of negro slaves to work them, and so ultimately of the American Civil War and all its attendant and subsequent miseries.

In 1733 the "Orangery" or Greenhouse, which included a living-house for the gardener, was completed by subscription, towards which the Society's old rivals the College of Physicians generously contributed £100 at the suggestion of Sir Hans. Five years later, in gratitude, the Court commissioned for the large sum of £280 the statue of Sir Hans by the sculptor Rysbrack which still stands at the centre of the garden. Payment for this was facilitated as the Company had opportunely just sold their South Sea Stock "with advantage" before the bubble burst. In 1745 the Royal College of Physicians invited the Apothecaries to collaborate in the preparation of the important Fifth Edition of the *British Pharmacopoeia*, which they did.

When Philip Miller died his deputy, William Forsyth, was appointed in his place. He also imported rare trees, plants and shrubs, including "the tree bearing the Jesuits' bark" and the cork tree which survives, appropriate to the Apothecaries' bottle of medicine. The shrub *Forsythia* was named in his honour. He resigned in 1784 to become the Superintendent of the Royal Gardens and his botanical demonstrator, William Curtis, was promoted in his place.

Curtis's duties had previously been largely in the educational sphere which the Society was developing for its apprentices. He was now, in addition,

The Apothecaries' drug mill at Battersea, c. 1840.

expected to superintend the garden, to encourage the study of botany "by all means both in theory and practice", demonstrate in the garden, supervise and instruct during the herbarising expeditions, and to lecture more frequently in the Hall. He was also in charge of the library and the repository of drugs and *materia medica*, and it was, moreover, his duty to prepare the specimens for the Royal Society each year. He was in addition "strongly recommended" to cultivate an extensive correspondence with distinguished botanists both at home and abroad. It was he who first introduced the sweet-smelling heliotrope (cherry-pie) and mignonette to the garden, and to England, in 1759. All this not surprisingly proved too much for his strength and he had to resign. During his tenure of office, however, he greatly improved the garden, inaugurating the present rock-garden for alpine plants with forty tons of masonry which had formed part of the old

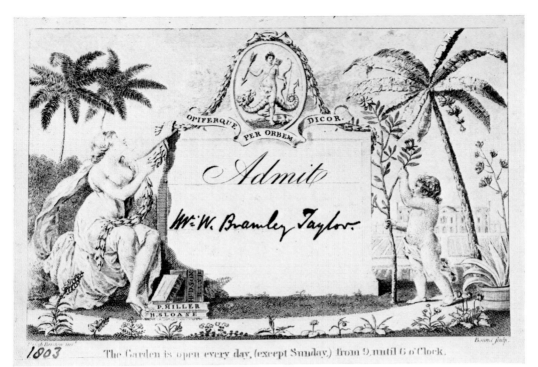

Admission ticket for members of the Society to the Physic Garden.

A view of the garden with the cedar trees looking north, 1840.

An Apothecary's jar with the Society's coat of arms.

*An Apothecary's mortar, 1625, made for Gideon De
Laune, at Whitechapel.*

Tower of London, supplemented with a heap of lava from Mount Hecla which Sir Joseph Banks, President of the Royal Society, and an old student at the Hall, had brought back as ballast from his exploration of Iceland. Sir Joseph also presented a quantity of seeds and plants from Botany Bay on his return from his voyage with Captain Cook. In 1771 Curtis started his *Botanical Magazine*, which immediately became a great success, and is still in publication.

By the end of the century, however, the garden was again in decline. The country was fighting for its life against the French and in 1798 the war was going badly. The Society's Minute Book has a modern ring when it decrees that economies must be made, "as the National affairs are in a Precarious situation". However, things improved once more during the next century. The garden maintained its fame and in 1803 two gold medals for botanical prowess in the final examinations were instituted at the suggestion of Sir Joseph Hooker, who also donated many rare trees and plants from the garden which he was forming at Kew for Princess Augusta, the mother of George III. In 1836 the celebrated botanist John Lindley, the Society's botanical professor, produced his *Introduction to the Natural System of Botany*, which superseded that of Linnaeus.

For a short time Robert Fortune then became curator, but left to undertake successfully the importation of 20,000 Chinese tea plants into India, the start of the modern tea trade. This he did with the use of the "Wardian case" which had recently been invented by Dr. Nathaniel Ward, F.R.S., Master of the Society. The collection of ferns at the garden is still housed in one of the surviving examples of this simple device. It was subsequently used to bring for the first time the chincona tree from the New World to India, and bananas from China to Fiji and elsewhere. About that time also we first hear of the use by the Society of the picturesque old "horse-mill" across the river in Battersea, where their drugs were ground before being sent to the Hall for final preparation.

When the Chelsea Embankment was built in 1874 the garden became cut off from the river. Its soil condition rapidly degenerated and many rare plants died. The cost of the garden again rose, and finally became too much for the Society's slender purse. The need for botanical study by medical students had by then become less imperative owing to scientific advances in chemistry and pharmacology, and the end came in the last year of the century. Neither the Royal Society nor the Royal College of Physicians were prepared to accept the burden of its maintenance, so to save it from being built over its responsibility was generously accepted by the Trustees of the London Parochial Charities, who still administer it through a curator and garden staff of eight under the jurisdiction of a Committee of Management on which the Society of Apothecaries is represented. Over three thousand students of botany and allied sciences visit the garden annually, and examination material is provided for medical schools and other examining bodies. Much valuable and sophisticated botanical and pharmacological research is currently carried out in the garden and in its laboratories, mostly by scientific teams from the University of London and its constituent colleges. But it is the Armorial bearings of the Society of Apothecaries which still adorn its gate.

A view of the Physic Garden from the river, 1795.

IV

Trouble
with
the
Physicians

ONE OF THE PRINCIPAL FUNCTIONS
of the Royal College of Physicians as expressed in their original Charter of
1518 had been the suppression of irregular and unlicenced medical practice,
which was very prevalent. To this end they were granted the monopoly of
practice in London and for seven miles around. As already mentioned, by
the middle of the seventeenth century with the growth of population it had
become the common practice of apothecaries to give advice with their
medicines without the intervention of a physician. Sir Francis Bacon, who
was professionally responsible for their new Charter, knew of this, but had
omitted any direct prohibition, as both he and the King rather disliked the
Physicians, and to annoy them they both openly showed their preference for
the Apothecaries in the struggle which developed between the two bodies.

The College had approved the proposal to separate the Apothecaries
from the Grocers in the belief that they would then be able to hold them in
subjection for their own purposes. The Apothecaries, however, were men of
stout courage and steadfastly pursued the basic question which was now
vital to the interests of both bodies—the ultimate legal right of the former to
act as medical attendants of the sick. The Apothecaries, although not forbidden to do so by their Charter, did agree that they did not possess the

further right to claim a fee for their services, and they continued to find their remuneration from the charges they made for their medicines. So the line which separated the apothecary from the physician in the eyes of the humbler sort of patient became increasingly obscured. As a result of this the status of the apothecary gradually rose and to some extent they actually began to supplant physicians even in the domestic households of the great.

Thus, in the reign of Charles I, as the result of a poison scandal, the College hastened to petition Parliament that all apothecaries in future be prohibited from compounding any medicinal substance other than upon the demand of a physician. One of the signatories of this was the great William Harvey, discoverer of the circulation of the blood. The Apothecaries replied that this, in addition to depriving them of their livelihood, would deprive the poor and the less well-to-do of medical aid, as physicians were few and their fees heavy—normally the gold coin called the Angel for each consultation. Culpepper is reputed to have said that physicians were like Balaam's ass—they would only speak when they saw an Angel. There were legal delays, and the dispute continued with increasing acrimony, the College now also accusing the Apothecaries of aiding the activities of quack doctors by dispensing their prescriptions. To this the Society replied that as Freemen of the City of London members were entitled to trade with all, and that in view of their seven years' training in pharmacy it would in their opinion be easier for a good apothecary to become a good physician than the reverse!

This truculent but sensible reply seems to have touched off unexpected liberal repercussions within the College itself, for we read in its *Annals* that one of the Censors advised his colleagues to consider whether, while seeking to reform others, they might not themselves sometimes be found delinquent?

The Privy Council was then approached to see how the differences between the two bodies might best be adjusted, but the outbreak of Civil War and the departure of the Court together with most Fellows of the College of Physicians from London removed the immediate threat to the Apothecaries, as the City and its Livery Companies, unlike the College, embraced the Parliamentary cause.

In spite of this the next few years were a period of difficulty for the Apothecaries, who had to contribute their quota towards the heavy financial demands of Cromwell's New Model Army along with the other City Companies. But on the whole they had increased in status by the time of the Restoration of Charles II. With the return of the monarchy the power of the College was also restored, but the Apothecaries, being by then more affluent and firmly established in the affections of the populace, were never again subjected to such dangerous threats to their existence.

The Society now informed the College that it thought it right and proper that at night, or when physicians were absent or loath to be disturbed, its members should practise medicine and advise the sick. The College replied with a demand that the Apothecaries' monopoly of dispensing should be abolished in favour of their own Licentiates and candidates. Quietly, compromise was reached. Then in 1666 the Plague struck. Most Fellows of the College again left London with their patrons, an action which they had reason to regret, but most Apothecaries stayed within the City. In the following year came the further calamity of the Great Fire when physician and apothecary alike had to flee.

On their return the Apothecaries rapidly rebuilt their Hall and re-established themselves, but the College made poor headway against the financial difficulties in which they now found themselves. They attributed much of this poverty which had suddenly fallen upon them to sharp practice on the part of the Apothecaries, who were increasingly and openly invading their legal monopoly of practice, refusing to accept their ancient status as "The Physician's Cooke", and prescribing independently for the poor or even visiting them professionally. A number of offensive pamphlets were published on both sides. On the side of the Physicians, for instance, Pope mented:

> For modern 'pothecaries taught the Art
> Through doctors' bills to play the doctors' part
> Bold in the practice of mistaken rules
> Prescribe, apply, and call their masters fools.

This was capped with less subtlety by Garth, who dubbed them as "mere greedy mechanicks and Empericks". He reported that:

> From files a random recipe they take
> And many deaths from one prescription make.

But in 1670 the Apothecaries again put out peace feelers, suggesting to

A satirical drawing of an Apothecary's shop.
Early 19th century.

the College that their ancient friendship should be revived and that they should promote jointly an Act of Parliament "for ye regulating of Physick, whereby to suppresse all Empericks and illegal Practisers and Makers of Physick, as common enemies to both". The Physicians were not to be won round so easily, however, as they knew that the public were increasingly calling in apothecaries direct and addressing them as Doctor, evidently considering them well qualified for this title. So five years later open war broke out again, and to harrass the Apothecaries they applied once again to Parliament for the sole right of conducting periodical "searches" of their shops and of destroying prescriptions or materials of which they did not approve. However, for this they were privately reprimanded by the formidable Lord Chancellor Jeffreys, who was then the official Visitor of the College. The Royal Society disapproved of this professional discord, but remained neutral to the extent that it recorded its abhorrence both of prescribing apothecaries and of dispensing physicians.

A number of the younger, brighter or more progressive Fellows of the College, John Radcliffe and Richard Mead amongst them, were also opposed to this continual profitless warfare between the two bodies, and it was Mead who started the practice of coffee-house consultations with the Apothecaries which laid the foundations both of his large fortune and of the future pattern of medical practice in England.

The Dispensary

Further dispute broke out in 1695 regarding the establishment in Warwick Lane by the Physicians of a new charitable voluntary dispensary for the sick poor of London, as they informed the Company that they expected their dispensary prescriptions to be compounded at a very low rate, which they themselves would determine. To this the Apothecaries refused to agree, partly because they doubted the Physicians' motives in establishing it. Eventually the frustrated College had to establish its own "laboratory" for this purpose and as the Apothecaries reported ". . . were imploying forreigners therein . . . to the prejudice of severall members of this Company and selling medicines in penny doses and boluses". The dispensary lasted until 1725, in which year the lease expired. After this it became the custom of the Physicians to devote themselves to charitable medical work in the wards of the newly founded voluntary hospitals of London, each of which also had its special Apothecary Shop on the premises which was under the jurisdiction of the Company.

The Rose Case

While the struggle with the College regarding their dispensary was at its height the Apothecaries secured a notable decision in the House of Lords which at long last established their legal right to practise. It was this case which determined their evolution into general practitioners of medicine during the following century. William Rose was a Liveryman of the Society of Apothecaries who practised from his shop in St. Martin-in-the-Fields. In 1701 he was sued by the College for treating a butcher named Seale without the intermediary of a physician, and the case was decided against him in the Queen's Bench Division. The House of Lords, however, reversed this decision in 1703, holding that despite the existing law it was not only contrary to custom but also against the public interest to prevent the giving

47

of advice and treatment by members of the Apothecaries' Company. Thus the age-old monopoly of the College was broken. Henceforward the apothecary who had served his apprenticeship could freely practise medicine without fear of persecution, as well as compound his remedies, although he had to wait for more than another century before he was permitted to make a direct charge for his advice as well as his medicine. It was in this way that the dispensing doctor arose, as did the British patients' continuing expectation of a routine bottle of medicine in addition to advice.

So the Apothecaries won the main issue of their long feud with the College. The other matters at issue had been mostly planned to annoy and keep them in subjection, and included such topics as the examination of their apprentices and the searching of apothecaries' shops. When Sir Hans Sloane became President of the College of Physicians these old bones of contention began to seem less vital, and relations between the two corporations became increasingly amicable.

The pharmaceutical apothecaries who did not directly aspire to medical practice remained the majority within the Company, however, until 1748, when Parliament failed to confirm the Apothecaries' own original monopoly of compounding prescriptions and selling drugs. This led to the main control of the retail pharmaceutical trade passing largely into the hands of the unqualified chemists and druggists who were uncontrolled either by the Society or the College. Although this naturally threatened the livelihood of the pharmaceutical apothecaries, it also tended to encourage the emergence of the medical element, and so led to the Society's resolution in 1774 which limited membership of its Livery to those members practising medically. The pharmaceutical apothecaries and the chemists and druggists eventually came together to establish the Pharmaceutical Society of Great Britain in 1841, leaving the Society then with an almost completely medical membership.

Thus from the trading outlook of a mercantile City Company interest had gradually veered throughout the eighteenth century, despite much opposition, towards a more academic and scientific attitude which was primarily concerned with educational problems of their medical apprentices in the fields of botany, *materia medica* and therapeutics. Throughout the nineteenth century considerable friendly co-operation was resumed between the College and the Company, particularly after the passing of the Apothecaries' Act of 1815, when the interest of both bodies in the improvement of

The title page of The Herball *by John Gerard*
(the Thomas Johnson edition).

July. 25th. 1816. —

189 MR. *John Keats* of full age — CANDIDATE for
a CERTIFICATE to practise as an APOTHECARY in *the country*. —

An APPRENTICE to MR. *Thomas Hammond of Edmonton*
APOTHECARY for *5* Years.
TESTIMONIAL from *Mr. Thos. Hammond* . —

LECTURES.

2 COURSES on ANATOMY and PHYSIOLOGY.
2 ——— THEORY and PRACTICE of MEDICINE.
2 ——— CHEMISTRY.
1 ——— MATERIA MEDICA.

HOSPITAL ATTENDANCE.

6 MONTHS at *Guy's & St. Thomas's*. —
as
MONTHS at

168 *Examined by Mr. Brande & approved*

The first Court of Examiners Book, showing the
entry for John Keats, 1816.

The Laboratory behind a pharmacy shop, c. 1840.

medical education was enhanced. Indeed, this Act's checkered passage might have come to a full stop at an early stage had not the College decided at the instance of Dr. George Mann Burrows and the Hon. George Rose, M.P., to support it, as the College of Surgeons had evinced little or no interest in the matter, while the chemists and druggists jealously opposed it.

ANNO QUINQUAGESIMO QUINTO

GEORGII III. REGIS.

∗∗

C A P. CXCIV.

An Act for better regulating the Practice of Apothecaries throughout *England* and *Wales*.

[12th *July* 1815.]

WHEREAS His Majesty King *James* the First, by Letters Patent, under the Great Seal of *Great Britain*, bearing Date the Sixth Day of *December*, in the Fifteenth Year of His Reign, did for Himself, His Heirs and Successors, grant unto *William Besse*, and divers other Persons therein named, and to all and singular other Persons whomsoever, brought up and skilful in the Art, Mystery, or Faculty of Apothecaries, and exercising the same Art, Mystery, or Faculty, then being Freemen of the Mystery of Grocers of the City of *London*, or being Freemen of any other Art, Mystery, or Faculty in the said City of *London* (so as they had been brought up and were' expert in the Art or Mystery of Apothecaries), that they, and all such Men of the said Art or Mystery of Apothecaries of and in the said City of *London* and Suburbs of the same, and within Seven Miles of the said City, might and should be one Body Corporate and Politic, in Substance, Deed, and Name, by the Name of the Master, Wardens, and Society of the Art and Mystery of Apothecaries of the City of *London*; and did ordain and declare, that by the same Name they might have perpetual Succession, and have, purchase, possess, enjoy, and retain Manors, Messuages, Lands, Tenements, Liberties, Privileges, Franchises, Jurisdictions, and Hereditaments to them and their Successors, in Fee Simple and Perpetuity, or for Term of Year or Years, or otherwise howsoever; and also Goods and Chattels, and all

Charter by Jac. 1. to the Apothecaries Company recited.

19 U

other

V

The Apothecary "Arrives"

As happens in most walks of life, the social status of the apothecary varied from time to time. Prior to receiving their Charter they were submerged in the Grocers' Company, but some grew rich through the importing and selling of rare drugs—"the Coach-Keeping Apothecary"—and many achieved considerable civic status. In a document of 1580, however, the grocer-apothecaries are described (by the College of Physicians) as being "ignorant and un-latined and of a mechanical education unlearned in true science", but this was presumably a biased judgement.

When James I granted a Royal Charter the Apothecaries as a whole rose in the world, being, as he expressed it, a special trade which concerned the lives and health of his good subjects. Towards the end of the seventeenth century their status in the City was respectable and the Company included several members of Aldermanic rank, while two of its Masters also became Members of Parliament. The rank and file remained mostly humble people, however—small tradesmen, but with big ideas!

The ambition and tendency of most apothecaries at this period was to act not merely as traders, but also as medical practitioners in cases of emergency or for minor ailments amongst the poor, who, respecting their seven years of apprenticeship training, were beginning to call them in when sick. This infringement of their College's monopoly was sharply contested by the Physicians, who often branded them as "lawless life-endangering quacks". But professional ambitions had been planted, and after the Rose case in 1704 had given them a legal right to practise medicine these took firm root. It is from this year onwards that the general practitioner or family doctor began to emerge. More and more apothecaries took up medical practice and fewer kept retail shops, particularly after the refusal of Parliament to pass the Bill granting them the monopoly of pharmaceutical retail trade in 1748. Then in 1774 the Court decided to restrict the Livery to those members of the Company who were practising medicine. Many apothecaries who did not wish to do so not unnaturally felt ostracised by their fellow members and eventually joined forces with their erstwhile despised rivals and enemies, the unincorporated chemists and druggists, and so often inaugurated important commercial partnerships.

The passing of the Apothecaries' Act of 1815, whereby the Society suddenly found itself in control of all general medical practice in the country, introduced a period of controversial and constructive effort by the Society, and the Court's interest naturally became further centred upon their practising members. Its endeavours were largely aimed at advancing the standards of therapeutics and the better education of the apprentices.

It was for such reasons that the remaining dissident faction of the Society's membership, under the leadership of the quaker, Jacob Bell (later M.P. for St. Albans), formally in 1841 joined with the most respectable of the chemists and druggists to set up an independent representative body, the present Pharmaceutical Society of Great Britain. This naturally fostered the rise of the great pharmaceutical drug houses at the expense of the Society's laboratories, a process which was greatly aided in the present century by the need for larger wholesale production and bulk dispensing as the result of the Insurance Act of 1911 and the extension of state hospitals. The Apothecaries finally gave up the commercial struggle in 1922, closing their retail shop in the Courtyard, and remained content to be a purely medical body.

The botanical basis of their trade had also led some apothecaries into the scientific field. The world's oldest and most distinguished scientific body, the Royal Society, was started in 1653 in the house of an Oxford apothecary named John Crosse and several were original members. Six Masters and more than eighty members of the Society have subsequently been elected Fellows. John Meeres, junior, son of the Society's first Clerk, was also elected F.R.S. in 1726. Being legally qualified, he was responsible for the formalities involved in the gift of the freehold of the Physic Garden from Sir Hans Sloane to the Society. He left the Society £200 to forward botanical work, and six silver candlesticks which are still used in the Hall.

In the mid-eighteenth century—as rivalry diminished—members of the College of Physicians and the Society inevitably became associated professionally, and later socially, as the Apothecaries adopted the principles of a "liberal education" and became more highly thought of professionally. There had previously been no prestige attaching to purely technical education, and this feeling had to be overcome before social standing could be improved. We read, however, in John Stow's *Survey of London* (1755) that "the Apothecaries are now recognised in private life by Physicians as fellow practitioners of a more modest standing", while in 1715 the Duke of Marlborough, with the approval of Queen Anne, had in defiance of parliamentary opinion appointed Isaac Teale to a newly created post termed Apothecary-General of all his armies. Adam Smith (1790) aptly described apothecaries as "the physicians of the poor at all times and of the rich when the danger is not very great". In 1803 Percival in the first book on medical ethics states that in sickness "the Apothecary is the precursor of the Physician to whom he . . . can prove a valuable auxiliary: the third of the three orders within one whole". All this was bringing them within sight of true professional status, although their remaining links with trade rendered them still objects of some suspicion to the class-conscious protagonists of social reaction throughout most of the nineteenth century. They gradually increased in learning, respectability and social status, however, and it is interesting to dip into one or two contemporary publications and see what the impartial world of that time thought of its apothecaries.

Of the father of Dr. Samuel Parr, Headmaster-designate of Harrow, who was called "The Whig Dr. Johnson", in 1766 we read: "As a surgeon-Apothecary Mr. Parr pursued a trade still regarded as subservient and inferior to the profession of the Physician, but skill and respectability could make an apothecary a man of some consequence in his neighbourhood." The physician had always stood out in social and academic estimation alongside the luminaries of the Church and Law. The Apothecaries still had a long way to go, and like their colleagues the Attorneys, "The G.P.'s of the law", they tended to model their professional attitudes upon those of their superiors respectively in Medicine and the Law, and their social mores upon the ways of the landed gentry, then the all-powerful arbiters of taste and learning. Jane Austen reassuringly mentions in *Emma* (1816) that "Mr. Perry the Apothecary was an intelligent, gentleman-like man whose frequent visits were one of the greatest comforts of Mr. Woodhouse's life".

The apothecary won through eventually, achieving his final status as the respected family general practitioner of medicine; the attorney under the complete domination of judges and barristers, and perhaps enjoying a more questionable reputation in general, had to change his name by Act of Parliament to "solicitor" before he could follow the same route to independence and public trust in the status of what the then Home Secretary termed as "self-governing middling sort of people".

Next, admirers of Mr. Jorrocks's *Handley Cross* will remember that the flourishing watering-place of that name was founded around 1840 by two practising apothecaries of opposing personalities. One, Roger Swizzle, was "a roystering, red-faced, round-about apothecary who had somewhat impaired his constitution by his jolly performances whilst walking the hospitals in London, and had settled at Appledore, a small market town in the Vale, where he enjoyed a considerable want of practice. . . . The Doctor's practice grew with the growth of Handley Cross . . . but a thriving trade soon brings competition—another patientless apothecary, Dr. Sebastian Mello, appeared. He was about forty, and was Swizzle's opposite in every particular being pale, thoughtful and studiously attentive to his dress. In imitation of the old-fashioned town physicians he carried a massive gold-headed cane. He could talk and flatter any serious minded woman into a belief that they were almost as clever as himself."

Tertius Lydgate, the provincial apothecary-G.P. hero of George Eliot's novel of the eighteen-thirties, *Middlemarch*, was perhaps rather ahead of his time. Indeed, the author states that "it was the general impression that Lydgate was not altogether a common country Doctor". He was a protagonist of the growing demand for reform within his profession, and so antagonised his provincial colleagues. He advocated the need for regular medical teaching and examinations, in addition to apprenticeship. Moreover, he used a stethoscope; 'an instrument which had not become a matter of course in practice at that time". His most important patient, Lady Chettam, approved of him rather grudgingly: "Yes, he is well-connected—one does not expect it in a practitioner of that kind. For my own part I like a medical man more on a footing with the servants, they are often all the cleverer."

Indeed, for a majority of country practitioners their status in 1840 was still merely that of a skilled tradesman, since their qualifying body, the Society of Apothecaries, was no university corporation but a Livery Company of the City of London. They were, moreover, still not yet legally entitled to charge for advice without medicine, so as compulsory vendors of medicinal potions they could not be "real" professional men. Later, as the statuatory fee authorised was only 2s. 6d. per visit, they were still unable for financial reasons to hand over their retail dispensing trade to the chemists or druggists until the passing of the Medical Act of 1858. After this the Apothecaries left their shops and became "proper doctors", while the druggists, stifling their similar ambitions to pursue the road to medical practice, remained in theirs and became pharmaceutical chemists. As late as 1879, however, the metamorphosis was incomplete, for a correspondent complained in the *Lancet* that "some members of the profession still maintain shops in which tooth-brushes or hair-oil may be purchased"!

Nonetheless it was said that the social status of the English medical man at this later period was the highest in Europe. It may be doubted, however, whether this thought was of much comfort to the struggling practitioners in the new towns spawned by the Industral Revolution and population explosion of mid-century. It was, however, the opinion of the aristocratic President of the College of Physicians that "the station of an apothecary (or a surgeon) could now be considered as that of a gentleman, and that such of them as had superior minds might even become ornaments of Society". This comforting assurance had not, however, presumably applied to the armed services, in which most medical officers had been appointed by warrant, and not commissioned, until well after the reorganisation which followed the scandals of the Crimean War. Moreover, one may remember that the Royal Apothecary himself was still requested to use the back entrance to the Palace on his professional visits!

Reform

During the early part of the nineteenth century throughout the country economic and social "revolution, renovation and reform" was in the air, and this spirit stirred also within the ranks of practising apothecaries and other professional men. In 1810 the Society had sent a memo to the Treasury, in which it stated categorically that "the medical practice in this country needs reform, is capable of much reform, and the general welfare of the Nation demands that reform . . ." No such expression of opinion was heard from the Colleges of Physicians or Surgeons. It was Dr. Edward Harrison, who practised in a small village in Lincolnshire, who formed the "Committee of the Associated Apothecaries", originally to protest against a Government tax on glass which threatened to increase greatly the price of medicine bottles. From that small start they went on to propose the formation of a single controlling body for G.P.'s and surgeons, in which they forestalled the present generation by their suggestion that it be called "The College of General Practitioners". These activities culminated in the Apothecaries' Act of 1815, which represented the first attempt by the legislature to control medical practice since the reign of Henry VIII. New educational ideas were now afoot and sanitary reform together with improved Poor Laws were pioneered, often by laymen. Professional books were also becoming more widely available. Communications and travel were easier. After the Reform Act of 1832 the middle-class electorate was greatly increased, and this included the 30,000 medical practitioners, mostly apothecaries or surgeon-apothecaries, whose political and professional influence could be mobilised for the first time. Thomas Wakely, Charles Hastings, and other radical medicos had stirred up a new pugnacity which demanded specified educational reforms and some common professional organisation; this resulted in the formation of the *Lancet* as their mouthpiece. They founded the provincial medical association which was the precursor of the B.M.A. and which for the first time provided a focal point for doctors' allegiance beyond their period of attachment to hospital or other teaching bodies, through which up-to-date ideas could gain currency and pressure be brought to bear on politicians.

In 1834 the Select Committee on Medical Education, while praising the work of the Society of Apothecaries, suggested that it had not the resources to institute the augmented educational courses becoming necessary for the various branches of medicine, surgery and midwifery advocated by men such as Lydgate. The Apothecaries continued, however, to conduct the final professional qualifying exams whilst the newly founded London

The OATH of a Freeman of the Company of Apothecaries, London.

YOU shall swear to be good and true to Our Sovereign Lord King GEORGE, and to be obedient unto the Master and Wardens of this Company in all lawful manner; you shall also keep secret all the lawful Council of this Fellowship; and all manner of Rules, Impositions and Ordinances that be made, or hereafter shall be made and lawfully ordained, for the good ordering of the said Fellowship, you shall well and truly observe and keep; and to your Power you shall be well-willing, helping and furthering to the good Government and Wealth of the said Fellowship, and shall not be Party or Privy in any Counsel or Device that may be to the Hurt or Hindrance of the said Company, or to the overthrowing and breaking of the good Laws and Ordinances of the same, but all such Practices, Counsels and Devices you shall disclose to the Master and Wardens of the said Company, and them labour to hinder and break so much as in you lieth.

So help You, God.

The Oath taken by Freemen of the Society.

University took on this larger educational task with the Society's co-operation, and a few years later were allowed also to award their own degrees.

It had previously been generally assumed that with a "liberal education" the professional aspects both of Medicine and the Law could easily be acquired by the intelligent student for himself: "The examiners only sought to find out what a young man knows, without seeking to inquire how he knows it." With so little formal academic professional education available, the apothecary's apprentice for practical purposes seemed lucky in that his teachers had closer touch with the sick population than the young physician's more academic superiors.

The provinces

In the midst of all these educational excitements, which were largely centred on London, it was the Apothecaries who first realised the professional isolation of the medical staff of provincial hospitals. Although the current advances in science were to some extent absorbed by them, they were unable to provide any educational facilities. No generally recognised professional standards or examinations other than those set by the Apothecaries yet existed. So the Society set out to encourage the formation of provincial medical schools where students could be adequately trained, and need only come to London for the final qualifying examination, which was to be of a high standard. Thus its qualification remained the most popular throughout the country until the end of the century. Almost every new university established in England during the nineteenth century began as a medical school established to satisfy the regulations of the Society's examiners.

The Home Secretary, Lord Sydenham, himself the son of a provincial doctor, thought with unfashionable democracy that "these improved arrangements redounded to the benefit of the middle-classes of people, who being the larger part of the Nation may be esteemed the most important". He also pointed out at a later date with considerable condescension that in the provincial towns "Doctors and Attorneys are well in the lead over other occupations and take a foremost place in middle-class urban Society, generally with some claim to gentility. . . ."

In 1873 about a hundred provincial hospitals providing some instruction and forty-three medical schools had come into being and were on the Society's list. All of these they strictly inspected. In 1851 St. Mary's Hospital opened in London with a distinguished medical staff and one hundred and fifty beds, but as no resident Apothecary had yet been appointed they were refused recognition until this was done!

The first woman doctor

In 1865 an event took place in the Apothecaries' Hall which made medical history. Miss Elizabeth Garrett, later Dr. Elizabeth Garrett-Anderson (1836–1917), after passing the examination for the Society's Licence, became the first woman to gain an English registerable qualification. This accomplishment caused great surprise and consternation throughout the country, and had only proved possible because the Founding Fathers had not contemplated the possibility of a woman applying when they drew up their regulations. The Diploma was awarded most unwillingly, and the Regulations were promptly amended in such a way that further female applicants were discouraged for many years to come. Nevertheless, as we now know, the woman doctor had "arrived". Her colleague and friend, Sophia Jex-Blake, also qualified a few years later from Edinburgh, and together they founded the Royal Free Medical School and Hospital for Women. Thus it was through the Society of Apothecaries that this new page of medical history came to be written. It was not until 1947 that the Society, by then more liberal-minded, obtained the permission of the City of London to admit women medicos as Freemen. Amongst the first to be elected was Dame Hilda Lloyd, at that time President of the Royal College of Gynaecologists and Obstetricians. There are at the present about twenty-five female Apothecaries.

In spite of its preoccupation with the complexities and responsibilities of medical politics, education and status, the Society never lost its interest and involvement in its civic status as one of the well-respected Livery Companies of the City of London. Indeed, in 1911 it provided for the first, and last, time the City's Lord Mayor, Sir Thomas Crosby, a distinguished general practitioner in Fenchurch Street. Throughout the centuries it continued like other civic bodies to present "loyal addresses" on the accession and death of monarchs (as well as on the occasions of George III's recovery from his attacks of madness). In common with most City Companies, in 1803 they sent a deputation to protest to the Government against the institution of the Income Tax; and during periods of national distress they opened a soup kitchen for the needy poor in their Courtyard.

So we have seen the slow emergence of today's medical practitioner from the Elizabethan grocer who also compounded pills and potions; an evolution in which the Society of Apothecaries played the leading role. As Underwood has said, "the lives of Englishmen have been ruled more by custom than plan, and so the medical profession had developed in a way unlike anywhere else in Europe. For a City Mercantile Company to have been entrusted by the State with the control of a learned profession, as were the Apothecaries by virtue of the Act of 1815, might seem inconceivable". The task was, however, willingly undertaken and, perhaps somewhat to their own surprise, was brilliantly carried through. Thus the erstwhile products

59

of the City apprenticeship system achieved that professional status which had for so long been their ambition, even if the highest ranks and the greatest professional prizes were seldom to be theirs. But it was not until the last "stigma" of trade had been eliminated by the Medical Act of 1886, which abolished the dispensing apothecary who lived partly on the sale of his medicines, that practitioners qualified by the Society could show clear title to rank as members of a learned profession and claim the status that such a title implied in Victorian England.

To define professional status exactly is difficult, although its marks have been said to be independence, intelligence and morality, blended no doubt with some self-interest, and a degree of public spirit which is rather modern. Owing, however, to Medicine's very tenuous connection with the State in the course of its evolution, unlike its sister profession of the Law, no high-ranking official posts in the hierarchy of the Establishment fell to its members by

The Society's arms, from a pill slab.

right, and so its leaders have always tended to lack that official and social recognition accorded to such people as judges and bishops. None the less, in compensation, members of the medical profession have by and large tended to attract more widespread respect and admiration from the general public than has throughout history generally been shown to the other learned professions, which should be compensation indeed.

VI

Medical Education is Developed

By AN EDICT OF QUEEN ELIZABETH I every trade was to be learnt by apprenticeship, which must last for seven years, and this had included the Apothecaries who were then incorporated within the Grocers' Company. Apothecarial apprentices, although performing those menial duties common to that status, were also instructed in the mystery, art or craft of compounding and preparing drugs and simples, which at that period when polypharmacy was the fashion could be a complicated and exacting accomplishment. They were also expected to be able to collect and recognise useful medicinal plants where they grew in the woods and meadows of what was then a largely rural countryside. At a later date, to assist the essential botanical education of apprentices, and as post-graduate education for members of the Livery and Court, as the science of botany progressed, "herbarising expeditions" were instituted. Six times a year the party would meet, generally in the yard of St. Paul's at 5 a.m., and follow their leader and demonstrator, collecting specimens and discussing their uses. At about 5 p.m. they would return to the Hall, where they would lay out their specimens and receive a short disertation from the demonstrator before partaking of a "sober repast". This was generally paid for by the Master on the first occasion; on subsequent excursions a small contribution was collected from each of those attending. However, as riotous and unseemly conduct sometimes ruled, the number of expeditions was reduced to two a year at which every apprentice who joined had to be "spoken for" by his master. Even then it was reported that some apprentices did not arrive on the scene until the hour appointed for their free dinner!

As London spread out into the country such expeditions became less rewarding and the distance to be travelled greater. By now the Society had achieved the status of owning a State Barge, however, of which the primary purpose was to carry the Master and his Court in the Lord Mayor's processions on important occasions. It was pressed into service also to conduct the herbarising expeditions along the river, often as far down as Gravesend and as high as Twickenham or beyond, as well as to and from the Physic Garden.

As mentioned in the last chapter, the members of the Court of the Society had always been much concerned with the proper education of its members' apprentices, and had seen to it that their masters gave them adequate practical instruction. This became increasingly so after 1704, the year in which their freedom to practise medicine had received legal sanction. They themselves also supervised the intellectual and moral calibre of all those who were bound apprentice, rejecting some and deferring many "until such time as they had improved themselves sufficiently to merit admission to this Company". They also conducted an oral examination in the Great Hall, open to all members to attend, every six months, which had to be passed by the apprentice before he was made free of the Society and so allowed to set up on his own. They rightly felt that a high standard of professional knowledge and skill must be *sine qua non* if their aspirations to future professional and social status were to materialise.

Practical education of the apprentice

By accompanying his master on his rounds the budding apothecary had considerably more practical opportunity of becoming familiar with patients and their diseases than had the academically circumscribed medical student of Oxford or Cambridge. It is true that like other apprentices he was condemned to much menial drudgery, and his sleeping quarters, if not under the counter of his master's shop, would be in an attic such as can be seen still in the Apprentices' Dormitory in the Hall. However, as he paid a fee which was often considerable for his tuition, he generally lived in other respects as one of the family, and often married one of the daughters.

On his rounds the eighteenth-century apothecary would still carry out the wishes of the physicians in charge of the patients, and these would include such varied procedures as blood-letting, tooth-drawing, the administration of enemata, blisters, fermentations and plasters, and cupping glasses. His apprentice would also be taught to recognise *materia medica* and to practise the still complicated art of compounding and dispensing medicines and simples of various types. He would keep such notes as his master required, and would assist in the occasional post-mortem examination.

The Society had established its chemical laboratory in 1672, where the industrious apprentice could also learn the rudiments of this new and important science. It was situated somewhat precariously beneath the Great Hall and many complaints were received regarding the fumes of sulphur and other nauseous gases which it generated. He would still attend the herbarising expeditions into the surrounding country and the Physic Garden to study botany, while he received his practical instruction in pharmacy and *materia medica* from his master. Books and herbals were now published in English, so that he could supplement his practical experience with theory, including that of anatomy. Dissections could be attended in the Surgeons' Hall, but systematic lecture courses were not yet generally fashionable. Apprentices in the City had always been under an order imposing celibacy, which perhaps gave some of them more time to devote to study. Evidently the Society selected them with care, for the records contain mention of very few black sheep, although we learn that one, Simon Stratford, was deported for "infamous practices" in 1768.

Apprenticeship was not the only route to the Freedom, however, for the son of a Liveryman could be admitted by Patrimony provided he could pass the examination and pay the enhanced requisite fee. In 1727 the unmarried daughter of a deceased Freeman surprised the Court by applying for admission. As civic law or Charter did not specifically forbid the entrance of a woman (such a contingency had never been envisaged), they decided that "her technical qualifications were inadequate", and paid generously for her admission to another Company. The Freedom could also be obtained then as now by "redemption", and in special cases by "gift".

*Dr. Richard Mead (1673–1754) who inaugurated
medical consultation with Apothecaries.*

Elizabeth Garrett Anderson (1836–1917), first
British woman doctor. Qualified at Apothecaries'
Hall, 1865.

Examinations

By the terms of the Charter the final oral examination of apprentices was supposed to be conducted twice a year jointly by the Master and Wardens with the President of the College of Physicians and one of his Censors present. As can be imagined, this led to considerable friction between the two bodies, but it is indicative of the Company's desire to maintain a good educational standard that they never sought its revision. Unlike the surgeons, they had always insisted upon some knowledge of Latin, which was at that time the lingua franca of science and medicine, and was necessary for deciphering medical prescriptions and instructions.

The physician Garth's Hogarthian and much-quoted reference to the Apothecaries' Hall where the examinations were conducted need not be considered as being disinterested:

> High, where Fleet ditch descends in sable streams
> To wash the sooty Naiads in the Thames
> There stands a structure on a rising hill,
> Where students take their licence out to kill.

There is, in fact, no evidence that the qualified apothecary killed more patients than did his more learned superiors the physicians!

The apprenticeship system, perfected by the Apothecaries, lasted for two hundred years, and in Cameron's opinion (1956) "constituted the most notable educational attempt in England to supply a comprehensive vocational training". Until the Act of 1815 it left an indelible and beneficient impress on British medical education and the modern system of clerking on medical "firms" in hospital perpetuates this practice.

With the age of the great explorers and navigators strange new medicinal plants had been brought home which had to be studied, and many could now be grown in the Society's Physic Garden on the waterfront at the village of Chelsea, four miles by water from its Hall (see Chapter III). It is reported in the minutes that the curator "by various ingenious devices would make exotic plants and herbs to grow". The purpose of this garden as already mentioned was twofold. It was to provide the *materia medica* for the Society's laboratory, where these were prepared for sale to practising physicians and apothecaries as well as to corporations; and throughout the eighteenth century also to the Army, Navy and East India Company. Its second and ultimately principal purpose had always been the education of its apprentices, and to this end the curator was expected to assist, and a demonstrator was appointed and paid by the Court both to lead the herborising parties and to lecture in the Hall. During the latter part of the nineteenth century a Professor of Botany and Materia Medica (and another of Chemistry) were also appointed, and several gold and silver medals were awarded annually on the results of the examinations, as the science of therapeutics was at that time still very largely based upon drugs of vegetable origin. The examination system which finally evolved from this scheme of instruction has been referred to as "a major historical landmark which marked the end of the era of eighteenth-century educational thought in this country".

The Apothecaries Act of 1815

"The Charter of Medical Reform", which after a somewhat checkered career received the Royal Assent just a month after the battle of Waterloo, threw enormous additional responsibilities of a hitherto unprecedented nature on to the Society, which they accepted and implemented in model fashion, particularly in the field of technical professional education. As Cope has said (1956), "our Society had greatness thrust upon it", and it remained the controlling body in medical education for almost the next fifty years. Thus it became the first professional body in this country to evolve and establish an organised system of education, qualification and registration on modern lines. The Apothecaries, having become general medical practitioners, then also held for the first time a legally recognised qualification in medicine, surgery and midwifery. This remarkable Act gave statutory form to some new ideas regarding professional status and ethics. It gave the Company the power to determine the educational necessities for apprenticeship, to examine for proficiency, and on the result of such examination to grant or withhold the Diploma which alone would authorise its holder to call himself an apothecary or general practitioner, and prevent the unqualified from doing so throughout England and Wales. This gave them healthy self-government and also protected them from rival professional organisations during this period of development. It was quite a near approach to that "closed shop" which is the ultimate ambition of all privileged bodies! The Society used its power wisely, however, and when the General Medical Council supplanted it in many of its functions in 1858 it paid generous tribute to the Society, and its rulers the Court, who, it said, were "forward-looking innovators in the field of education and had moreover shown a certain spirit of altruism in undertaking these tasks".

The first action of the Court after the passing of the 1815 Act was to appoint a panel of twelve examiners, including the energetic apothecary-physician George Mann Burrows, one of the pioneers of medical educational reform. This panel drew up the first course of professional studies ever to be prescribed in detail. They met every Friday for eleven months in the year, and the minutes record that absence of any was very rare. Their special *desiderata* included in addition to a competent knowledge of Latin a certificate of attendance at lectures in anatomy and physiology, medicine, chemistry and *materia medica*. They also shortened the apprentices' course by two years and decreed that that period should be spent "walking the hospitals" with physicians and surgeons. Their oral qualifying examinations were serious attempts to test knowledge, and were no longer the informal interviews with perfunctory questioning such as the Royal College of Physicians still favoured. They rejected no less than 15 per cent of candidates during the years 1815–34, while steadily raising the standards. The number of successful candidates averaged 400–500 per annum for many years. By 1835 the curriculum had been stabilised and began to look modern, with the incorporation of much of the rapidly increasing body of scientific knowledge which was becoming available. In 1839 they instituted the first written examination, an innovation which was said to have been "much appreciated" and which was soon copied by the Civil Service and the other professional corporations, and remains with us today.

One of the major imperfections of the initial training programme was that no provision was made for actually teaching midwifery. Child-bearing had always been regarded as a natural function of women, and not as a process calling for qualified medical aid, although some male midwives were in practice and were tolerated by the profession. Gradually, however, the high infantile mortality, which had been taken for granted throughout previous centuries, came under criticism, and the idea grew that at least some of it might be preventable. Thus in 1827 the Society, again in the forefront of progress, instituted an examination in midwifery and the diseases of women and children, and so initiated practical instruction in these subjects. It also published the first register of medical students shortly afterwards, and in 1845 *The Medical Directory* appeared, whereby the (professional) sheep could be distinguished from the goats who were still flourishing greatly among both rich and poor.

Soon after this it became usual for apothecaries in general practice to take a diploma at the Surgeons' Hall in addition to the L.S.A., and as the surgeons failed in their efforts to obtain a similar Act they in their turn had to take the L.S.A. if they wished to become general practitioners. Such men were referred to as surgeon-apothecaries, and were well equipped to engage in all the usual branches of general practice. This was the state of affairs in 1884 when the Conjoint Board was formed by the two Royal Colleges.

It is evident that the Society's influence and work vastly raised the standard of medical education, practice and ethics throughout the country. The status of these new family doctors was also established both in London

SCIENTIFIC CONVERSAZIONE AT APOTHECARIES' HALL.

A soirée at Apothecaries' Hall.
Illustrated London News, 1855.

68

and the provinces. As the "die-hard" Sir Henry Halford, P.R.C.P., said in 1834: "I was one of those that was sorry that the power was given out of the hands of the physicians to license practitioners of that description, but since they have had it I must do the Apothecaries the justice to say that they have executed that Act extremely well and that the character of that branch of the profession has been amazingly raised since they have had that authority."

In 1828 the University of London was founded and its first Faculty was that of Medicine. The authorities consulted the Society regarding their proposal to institute courses of medical education, and we read of the satisfactory agreement which was arrived at between them "whereby a plan of medical education was devised, equally satisfactory to the Society and to the professors of the University". The University was not enabled to give degrees until 1836, so the majority of students continued to qualify with the Society's Diploma. The Society was asked to nominate two representatives to sit in the Senate (they still do), but gradually their teaching functions were taken over as the University grew, and were relinquished after the University built its two teaching hospitals (King's College Hospital, and University College Hospital). During this period between the two great Medical Acts the Apothecaries exerted a powerful and formative influence upon medical training and practice, and initiated the modern idea of statuatory professional educational qualification of acceptable standard, and with legal sanction. All this was entirely free of state control and remained so until the advent of the National Health Service in 1948.

The Medical Act

The second great Medical Act was passed in 1858. It resulted from "the continuing demand for further reform . . . like the resistless billows of the ocean, carrying all things before it", as the youthful *Lancet* picturesquely put it. The chief result of this Act was to establish the General Medical Council, which superseded the Society in its disciplinary function of controlling the activities of the profession. No new licensing authorities were sanctioned, but the standards of education and of existing diplomas or degrees within the United Kingdom were to be correlated and registered by the members. They had the right, after trial, to "strike off" offenders, and were responsible themselves only to the Privy Council. The Society still sends a representative to sit on this Council, and the L.S.A. Diploma, which changed its designation by Act of Parliament to its modern form L.M.S.S.A. (Licentiate in Medicine and Surgery of the Society of Apothecaries) in 1907, is still fully recognised by it.

Gradually with the establishment of efficient medical schools in London and the provinces the system of apprenticeship withered away, first in London and later in the provinces. By about 1870 it had been everywhere replaced by full-time medical studentship.

With the establishment of the G.M.C. the formative role of the Apothecaries in the educational field came to an end, but it had not proved inglorious. To quote again Sir Zachary Cope (1956), "The gracious way in which they (the Apothecaries) relinquished their responsible task did them as much honour as the readiness with which they performed the difficult duty put upon them for forty-three years previously. Since that time they have maintained their position as a responsible qualifying body sustained and encouraged by the records and memories leading back to the Golden Age when they wielded such a benevolent control over medical education in this country."

It was soon after the passing of this Act that the Society decided to establish a certificate in dispensing in order that G.P.s need no longer compound their own medicines. With the demise of the "dispensing doctor" during the present century holders of this qualification have been in great demand by hospitals, commercial bodies, and the Armed Forces. The certificate was recognised by the Ministry of Health when the National Health Service was introduced and its name was changed to "Technician in Pharmacy". It continued to flourish, and during 1966 the customary course of lectures was delivered and one hundred and seventy such certificates were subsequently awarded. Certain specialist post-graduate diplomas, each the first of its kind and of high standard, were later established by the Society. These included the Mastership in Midwifery, the Diploma in Industrial Health (D.I.H.) and in 1959 the Diploma in Medical Jurisprudence (D.M.J.). The Gillson Scholarship for original research in pathology is awarded annually, as is the Rogers Prize, and there are certain endowed lectureships, of which one of the most important is the "Strickland Goodall" in cardiology. The Society awards a gold medal for scientific advance in therapeutics annually, and several Nobel Laureates feature on its roll. Like other City Companies, it still maintains charitable funds for various purposes, and is represented on most important medical bodies, including the General Medical Council, the British Post-Graduate Medical Federation, and the Association for the Study of Medical Education. Symposia and courses of instruction both for specialists and G.P.s are also organised at the Hall. It was invited to submit a memorandum regarding the future of medical education to the Royal Commission, 1966.

In 1959 the Faculty of the History of Medicine and Pharmacy was founded within the Society. No similar academic body had existed anywhere in the Commonwealth to maintain interest in and knowledge of the history of the medical profession's fight against ignorance and disease through the ages, nor to maintain the traditions and ethic which are based upon this story. It seems strange that every Continental and many American universities have for long supported full Professorships in this subject.

The Society's Faculty has a number of endowed lectures, including that which commemorates its founder Gideon De Laune. Another designed to reinforce the historical ties between the City and the Society was endowed in 1966. It holds a panel of lecturers which it sends to medical schools, societies and corporations throughout the country on request. It has also established permanent lecturers in medical history in several medical schools in London and the provinces. The Maccabaean Prize and Medal is awarded annually for an essay by an undergraduate or graduate under 30. Its large membership, and attendance at all its functions and congresses, is evidence of the need which had previously existed for such a body. It was responsible for the "Doctor's Window" in Guildford Cathedral in which the Society's Arms occupy the central position. It also was honoured by an invitation to present a memorandum of its views to the Royal Commission on Medical Education in 1966.

It is pleasant to end this chapter with another quotation from Sir Zachary Cope's own Gideon De Laune lecture which he gave before the Society in 1956. He said: "There are few in this generation who realise what an important part the Society of Apothecaries has taken in the development of Medical Education in this country and in creating that type of practice which is a cause for legitimate pride."

VII

Some Eminent Apothecaries

I T HAS BEEN REMARKED IN A PRE-
vious chapter that throughout the ages the average apothecary has tended
to be a "middling sort of man", doing a good job quietly and well. As in all
types of community, however, some people achieve a greater prominence
than their fellows, and so it was in our Society.

The reputed founder of the Society, **Gideon De Laune,** was the son of a
refugee French Protestant pastor. He took degrees in medicine at Mont-
pellier and Paris and so was able to become a Licentiate of the Royal College
of Physicians and practise medicine in London. Gideon was born in 1565,
trained as an apothecary within the Grocers' Company and became attached
to the Court of James I as apothecary to his wife, Anne of Denmark. His
influence was sought by those apothecaries who wished to separate from the
Grocers' Company and form a corporation of their own. After consultation
with his colleague, the Royal Physician, Sir Theodore de Mayerne, also a
refugee from France, they solicited the King for a Charter of Incorporation for
the Apothecaries. The King, always anxious to appear on the side of Wisdom
and Science, agreed to this, thinking it advisable to "disunite, disjoin, separate
and dissociate the Apothecaries of our City" from the Grocers. There could be

*Sir Charles Dodds, Bt., F.R.S., twice Master of the
Society of Apothecaries. After a painting by Raymond Piper.*

The Court of Apothecaries in session, 1967.

no doubt about his wishes, and so eventually our Society was born out of that great Company.

As a foreigner, however, Gideon was debarred from becoming Master of the new Society until 1628 (and again in 1637) after being awarded the Freedom of the City of London by royal decree and becoming an Alderman. He was a great benefactor to the new body and contributed generously towards the building of its Hall. In gratitude for his benefactions the Society had a white marble bust made of him, which (since 1846) presides, from the great oak screen, over the Hall. The portrait of him, probably painted by Cornelius Janssen, a fashionable artist of that time, which hangs in the Court Room is said to have been saved by apprentices from the burning Hall during the Fire of London. He owned estates in Bedfordshire and London, as well as in Virginia and the Bermudas. He also owned the manor of Sharsted in Kent, where he still has descendants. He married Judith Chamberlaine, a member of the family which invented and maintained for several generations the secret of the obstetric forceps. They had a son and a daughter who both "married well". It was said that "he was much reputed for many singularities in his time", although their nature is not specified.

Much of De Laune's personal wealth was derived from the import of rare drugs and spices from the New World and from the recently opened-up countries of the East. He also manufactured a famous "wonder-pill" of which the formula was kept secret; its principal ingredient, however, is known to have been Colosynth, a powerful purgative. We hear that one hundred years later "his celebrated pill is in great request to this day, notwithstanding the swarms of pretenders to pill-making" (*see p.* 17). It was recorded by one of his relatives, although not altogether accurately, that "he lived piously to the age of 97 years, and was worth (notwithstanding his many acts of publick and private charity) near as many thousand pounds as he was years . . . having about 60 grand-children at his funeral (1659) which was arranged by the College of Arms".

Nothing could have been farther from the picture of the indigent apothecary, described by his contemporary Shakespeare, in *Romeo and Juliet*, who it will be remembered was "a needy man in tattered weeds—sharp misery had worn him to the bones . . . so bare and full of wretchedness"! Indeed, it has been thought that the acidulous Garth may have had De Laune in mind when he referred in his poem *The Dispensary* to:

73

> The sage in velvet chair who lolls at ease,
> To promise future health for present fees!

There followed a group of apothecaries whose interest and pioneer work within the new scientific field of botany gained them contemporary fame and should ensure that they are not forgotten by members of their Society.

John Parkinson (1567–1603) was a practising apothecary at the time when the Society's Charter was awarded. At the King's direction and possibly on the advice of De Laune, he was named as an original member of the Court of Assistants and was elected a Warden in 1620. He never became Master, however, as he resigned shortly afterwards. He was appointed by James I as Royal Apothecary and Charles I, who thought highly of him, gave him the title of "King's Botanist", *Botanicus Regius Primarius*. He cultivated a large garden "well stored with rarities" in Long Acre, which embraced some of present-day Covent Garden. He wrote two major herbals or gardening books, a species popular then as now, in which we obtain an excellent account of the simple drugs in use at that time and their sources. These were mostly of vegetable origin, but being pharmacologically with the times he includes the description of such a rare and desirable "wonder drug" as the unicorn's horn and its many important uses in medicine. He himself introduced seven new species of plant into England, while he described for the first time no less than thirty-three as growing within the U.K., adding thirteen to the hitherto recorded flora of his native Middlesex alone. A genus of leguminous trees was named *Parkinsonia* in his honour.

He was a friend of such worthy contemporaries as Tredescant, Sir Theodore de Mayerne and Thomas Johnson. The latter says of him in the introduction to his *Herball*, "John Parkinson an apothecarie of this City (yet living and labouring for the Common good) in the yeare 1629 set forth a worke by the name of *Paradisus in sole* wherein he gives the figures of all such plantes as are preserved in gardens for the beauty of their floures, and for meates or sauces; and also an Orchard of all trees bearing fruit . . . I could add nothing to what he had done upon that subject before." The title of that work constituted a pun "in merry mood" on his surname, *Paradisus* meaning a park, and *sole*, sun. It was dedicated to Queen Henrietta Maria, who is said to have written him a commendatory verse. In it he described nearly a thousand plants, and in his other great work *Theatrum Botanicum*, or

"The Theatre of Plantes" (1640) he included no less than 3,800. He was buried in St. Martin-in-the-Fields "with great pomp".

Parkinson's pupil **Thomas Johnson** (1604–44) was a popular and respected young apothecary practising on Snow Hill within the City of London when the Civil War broke out. He also tended a garden in which he grew medicinal herbs with which to supply his shop, as well as rare plants. He was a keen participant in the Society's herbarizing expeditions, and he published a short account of four of these, together with some thoughts upon the botanical training of apprentices. In 1633 he brought out a very much improved and enlarged edition of his colleague John Gerard's famous *Herball*. This monumental work of 1,400 folio pages (which weighs nearly a stone!) is still well known to botanists and bibliophiles, and copies are eagerly sought. It was greatly used in country houses, particularly during the eighteenth century, largely for the items of domestic medicine and self-medication which it contains, as well as the delightful woodcuts which illustrate no less than three thousand plants, shrubs, trees and roots. These were also used as a great source of design for art-needlework and even pottery. He presented a copy of this *Herball* to the Master and Wardens of the Society of Apothecaries as a mark of respect; they in turn made him a Liveryman and gave him a gown and hood to wear as symbols of his new status in the Company.

It was in the previous year that a friend lately returned from the Bahamas had presented him with a botanical novelty, a bunch of bananas, which he exhibited outside his shop, the first to be seen in this country. He was unaware that they were edible, but had their likeness engraved, and the result can be seen in the left bottom corner of the frontispiece to his *Herball* (*opp. p.* 48). At the outbreak of Civil War he left his botanical studies, and unlike most of his colleagues joined the Royalist Army. He proved popular and able, and rose to the rank of lieutenant-colonel. While stationed in Oxford he was awarded the D.M. degree by the University at the express wish of the King. He died of wounds after conducting a brave defence of Basing House in Hampshire. The prime purpose of his great book, he says, is for the use of "my loving friends and fellow Travellers" in the study of botany, "and of those apothecaries who ought to be ashamed of ignorance in a thing so absolutely necessary to their profession. They should indeed know these things as workmen do their tools, that is readily to call them by their

75

names, know where to fetch and whence to procure the best of each kind; and lastly how to handel them". He adds piously:

> Did God not helpe and into herbes infuse
> A working power, in vayne we medicines use.

It has been pleasantly said that the eponymous *Johnsonia* Group of lilies are his wreath, and the *Herball* his monument.

Brief mention should also be made of three further "botanical worthies", members of our Society, and celebrated in their day.

James Sherard, F.R.S. (1666–1738), was apprenticed as a young man to the renowned curator of the Society's Physic Garden, John Watts, and later, under his guidance, devoted himself to scientific botany after having made 'a substantial fortune' as a practising apothecary in Mark Lane. This enabled him to retire in 1720 and purchase a country estate at Eltham in Kent, where he cultivated rare and valuable plants. His home was much visited by Continental botanists. During this period he seems also to have qualified as a physician. In 1728 his brother died, leaving him as sole executor of his fortune. James thereupon employed it as his brother had wished in establishing a Chair of Botany in Oxford, together with the well-known Physic Garden alongside Magdalen Bridge. The University in gratitude conferred its D.M. upon him. As he decreed that the nomination of the Professor should lie with the Royal College of Physicians, this body on the recommendation of Sir Hans Sloane also conferred upon him its Fellowship "without examination or fee whatsoever". He never married, "and left £150,000 behind him". The *Dictionary of National Biography* states that Sherard was singularily accomplished, for in addition to being an excellent botanist he was also an amateur musician and violinist. He is said to have composed twenty-four sonatas "for violin, violoncello and bass; extended for the harpsichord".

He was the life long friend of **James Petiver,** F.R.S. (1658–1718), who became an eminent botanist and entymologist. He was born near Rugby and was educated there. While serving his apprenticeship to the Chief Apothecary at St. Bartholomew's Hospital he met the celebrated naturalist John Ray and catalogued his herbarium for him. They became intimate friends and Ray proposed him for election to the Royal Society on account of his botanical contributions to Camden's *Britannica*. He tended a notable

John Gerard (1545–1612) from his Herball or
General Historie of Plantes, 1597.

garden all his life at "The Sign of the White Cross" near Long Acre. The *D.N.B.* suggests that although his practice was extensive it may not have been very "classy", for he is known to have advertised a number of quack nostrums. Later he became Apothecary to the Charterhouse, where, as he then had more leisure, he formed a museum of miscellaneous objects of interest, including insects. This brought him a large international correspondence and reputation, although he used to complain that his business had never enabled him personally to travel farther afield than Hampstead. He was therefore much excited when in 1707 his uncle left him £7,000 to use for travel; and equally cast down when it was found that his half-brother, the sole executor, had himself made off with the legacy. In 1712, while demonstrator to the Society's Physic Garden, he consoled himself with what constituted his longest excursion, which took him to Bath and Bristol to seek rare plants, and later to Cambridge with his friend Sherard. He never married, and when he died his body "lay in State" at Cooks Hall for several days before burial in St. Botolph's Churchyard. Sir Hans Sloane was one of the six pall-bearers, and purchased his books and museum, which he presented later to the British Museum. His herbarium is in the Natural History Museum. It was said that "his distinction was that he first made science popular". He published *The London Herbal* (1707) and many other volumes, including one of the first on British butterflies (1717), as well as twenty-one papers in the *Philosophical Transactions* of the Royal Society.

Isaac Rand, F.R.S. (?–1743), who later became the Director of the Chelsea Physic Garden, was one of the thirteen young apothecaries who clubbed together and subscribed to the cost of building the wall—which still stands—around the Apothecaries' Garden in 1674 to prevent the "vandalism" to which it was being subjected. For a time he practised in Haymarket, but it is said that his hot, ungovernable temper necessitated his retirement in 1700. The *Randia* genus of red tropical plants were so named by Linnaeus after a contentious visit he paid to Rand at the garden in 1736. His personal botanical preference is said to have inclined him to the study of inconspicuous little plants, several of which he named for the first time.

At an earlier date the garden had been allowed by the Society to deteriorate, as it was then financially in low water, and Rand persuaded nineteen of his friends and colleagues to subscribe to restore it. These included Petiver (whom he succeeded as demonstrator of plants), Joseph Miller,

Samuel Doody, Adam Buddle (after whom the *Buddlea* is named), James Sherard, William Hudson (author of *Flora Anglica*, 1762), and John Lindley, whose *Natural System* of botany supplanted that of Linnaeus. All of these men achieved later distinction and several became F.R.S. As the result of this restoration the garden again became notable, and the post of *Praefectus Horti* (Director) was created for Rand at a salary of £100 p.a. It thus became his duty to transmit to the Royal Society, under the terms of Sir Hans Sloane's gift, the fifty varieties of plants grown annually in the garden. Needless to say, Rand's Directorship was punctuated with quarrels both with the Society and with his equally celebrated gardener, Philip Miller, who also became a Fellow of the Royal Society. He died in 1743 and his widow presented his library to the Society, several volumes of which are now kept at the garden, together with an endowment of fifty shillings annually to be paid to the Director of the Garden for use as he thought best. There is a portrait of him in the Hall.

The science of botany having been well and truly established, largely through the work and enthusiasm of the men just mentioned, let us now turn to a different and unique field in which the Society played a rôle.

John Keats (1795–1821), who must be considered the most famous person ever to qualify as an apothecary, only practised medicine for a year, although he studied for five years and qualified with distinction at the Hall at the age of 20, before devoting himself to poetry. He was little more than 25 years old when he died of self-diagnosed tuberculosis of the lungs. Little is known of his father, who was groom at the "Swan and Hoop" in Moorgate, married the proprietor's daughter and so became manager. John, the eldest son (a seven-month child), was devoted to his mother, and during her terminal illness sat up for several nights to give her food, medicines, and to read to her. At school, although rather solitary and always reading, he was popular and was a great boxer. On leaving school at the age of sixteen he was apprenticed for five years to Mr. Thomas Hammond, a surgeon in Edmonton. Mr. Hammond reported that his pupil demonstrated "a fine flow of animal spirits at most times". After four years he left to "walk the hospitals", choosing for this purpose the then combined St. Thomas's and Guy's. The notes he kept of anatomy and physiology lectures are in the Hampstead library and show him to have been soundly trained in the knowledge of the time. He confessed that occasionally at lecture "there came a sunbeam into the room and with it a whole troop of creatures floating in the ray, and I was off to Oberon and Fairyland"! A friend also wrote that "even in the Anatomy room I have seen Keats in a deep poetic dream, his mind was on Parnasus with the Muses". In his collected works is a long prose scrap in medieval form written during a lecture given by the famous surgeon Sir Astley Cooper. Sir Astley, however, recorded none the less that he had always been fond of "Little Keats", whom he described as being only just over five feet in height, good-looking, with reddy-brown hair.

He was able to produce the necessary certificates of diligent attendance at the courses in medicine, *materia medica*, chemistry, and anatomy and physiology within the minimum time possible, and at the earliest possible age, twenty-one, he presented himself in the first batch of candidates to be examined under the new regulations at the Apothecaries' Hall on July 25, 1816. It is recorded by Mr. Brande, his examiner (and later Master of the Company), that "he passed with ease; a creditable and talented performance", as he had, in fact, only completed four of the five years' apprenticeship. The Court therefore granted him their licence, but he had to wait until the end of October, when he reached the age of 21, before he could receive the Diploma (*see p.* 49).

On his return to Guy's he was awarded the coveted and responsible post of "dresser" to one of the three surgeons, Mr. William Lucas, and possibly subsequently to Sir Astley Cooper, who was then Europe's foremost surgeon. Operations at that time, without anaesthetics, were cruel, bloody ordeals, and it is little wonder that the sensitive, aesthetic Keats was nauseated and repulsed by this introduction to medical practice. He set up for a time in Hampstead, but by May 1817 he had decided to give up, "Not being suited by temperament for it. . . . My last operation was the opening of a man's temporal artery. I did it with the utmost nicety; but reflecting on what passed through my mind at that time my dexterity seemed a miracle, and I never will take up the lancet again."

When he announced his decision to his guardian, saying that his mind was full of his longing to become a poet and that he intended to rely for a livelihood on his ability to write, the latter retorted, "John, you are either mad or a fool to talk in so absurd a manner." Thenceforward he devoted himself feverishly to the company of literary friends and to poetry, with occasional periods of doubt born of practical necessity. In 1819, for instance, beset by

John Keats (1795–1821) from an etching by John Severn.

financial and domestic troubles, he wrote, "I have been at different times turning in my head whether I should go and study for a physician; I am afraid I should not take kindly to it again; I am sure I could not take fees—and yet I should like to do so"! A little later he was offered the post of surgeon on an East Indian trading ship, but refused after much heart-searching, saying rather ungratefully, "I would rather strain my nerves at some great poem than be a dunderheaded Indiaman." A few days later in a fit of depression he wrote to his sister that he was "preparing to enquire for a situation as an apothecary, but Mr. B. persuades me to try the press once more . . . I am really fit for nothing but literature . . . at no period have I acted with any self-will but in throwing up the Apothecarial pro-fession. That I do not repent of. This shall be my last trial; not succeeding I shall needs see what I can do more in the Apothecary line." He never regretted having studied medicine, however, as in doing so he felt that he had enlarged his knowledge of life, and he kept all his medical books "to look over again and keep alive the little I know thitherwards". His subsequent poetic works, however, apart from his powers of observation show little trace of the influence of his previous professional training, unless, as it has been said, poetry comes from emotion recollected in tranquillity.

A year later, in February 1820, he died from massive pulmonary haemorrhage, the result of tuberculosis of the lungs, caught no doubt from his brother, with whom he had shared "digs" and whom he had nursed devotedly until the time of his death in 1818. So ended prematurely and tragically this fascinating love-hate relationship between one of our greatest poets and the apothecarial and surgical professions. As Hale-White said, "His native industry made him work hard at medicine, but his heart was not in it. He knew that the gift of poetry was his and it was to this, after deciding that he would not make a good doctor, that he devoted the last few years of his short life, thereby enriching our national heritage." George Crabbe, a less eminent poet, was also educated as an apothecary—as were his near contemporaries, the novelist Tobias Smollett, and Elias Ashmole.

We now descend from "Parnassus" to the type of apothecary more usual in the Society; dedicated hard-working men bent on advancing the practice of better medicine and of improving the educational facilities for the profession.

John Nussey lived from 1794 to 1862. "Mr. Nussey was a conspicuous person," said the *B.M.J.* obituary notice. "He was of a Yorkshire family connected for upwards of a century with our Royal family. He was the favourite medical attendant of George IV and ever since received the favour and confidence of Royalty." He devoted his life to the interests of his profession. Having taken the L.S.A. in 1818, he was appointed seven years later Apothecary-in-Ordinary to the King, and he served William IV, Queen Victoria and Prince Albert in a similar position. "Few men of his time had more influence with the aristocratic portion of Society, whilst enjoying a lucrative practice, and esteem of his large circle of patients," claimed the *Lancet*. He practised in Cleveland Row, St. James's, in partnership with his fellow Royal Apothecary Mr. Du Pasquier; he was also for a time Visiting Apothecary to St. George's Hospital. On his appointment to the Royal household he successfully claimed a seat upon the Court of the Society, a claim which was not allowed, however, in the case of his successor. In this situation he was able to exert considerable influence, which favoured the status of the Apothecaries and their efforts to improve the medical curriculum.

The *Medical Times* wrote in 1862, "About 20 years ago when an English nobleman was murdered by his valet, there stood up one medical witness at the trial who after he had answered to his name added, 'I am an apothecary' . . . Mr. Nussey was proud of his calling and had good right to be so . . . the London Apothecaries during the last two centuries were good practitioners and had a high repute for scientific attainments . . . they had the cream of London practice in their hands . . . what they did, they did well."

In 1832 Nussey, who had risen to be Senior Warden of the Society, announced at a meeting of the Court of Assistants that at the Ascot races a discharged Greenwich pensioner with a grievance had that day hurled a stone at the King and hit him on the head, and induced the Society to forward a "dutiful address of Commiseration and congratulation, which was immediately graciously acknowledged".

During the next year, during his Mastership, his wife gave birth to a daughter, whereupon the Court subscribed for a silver loving-cup of value 25 guineas as a permanent memorial, "a like event not being previously recorded in the Annals of the Society". This is now on permanent loan to the Society and is used at its banquets. The handle of the lid is formed by the rhinoceros crest of the Society.

Nussey was active in the affairs of the Society and at one time conducted negotiations with the Government for an exchange of the Physic Garden for a portion of the newly established Gardens at Kew (1838). In 1845 he presented the "curious and ancient picture representing Queen Elizabeth reviewing her fleet after the defeat of the Spanish Armada", painted, it is believed, by Nicholas Hilliard, the famous miniaturist, in 1577, and described in Walpole's *Anecdotes*, which now hangs in the Entrance hall.

When the General Medical Council was formed under the Medical Act of 1858 Nussey was nominated by the Society as its first member, and was elected Treasurer; he served until 1861, when he was "compelled through age and infirm health to send in his resignation" and was succeeded by George Cooper, a surgeon and Licentiate of the Society. He attended Queen Victoria in several of her confinements, including that of the future Edward VII, and is said to have declined her offer of a baronetcy. As his obituary notice remarks: "He did much good in his generation, and paved the way for a better state of things to come." His Court dress and sword together with some other relics are preserved in the Royal College of Obstetricians and Gynaecologists in Regent's Park.

Space will not allow us to consider the many other distinguished figures associated with the Society during the long reign of Queen Victoria, although these included such figures as Dr. Thomas Addison (of Addison's disease), Sir William Jenner and Sir James Clarke, who attended the Prince Consort in his last illness, Sir Alfred Garrod, T. H. Huxley and Dr. Andrew Ure, F.R.S., one of the pioneers of the Industrial Revolution. A brief exception may be made in the case of **John Hughlings Jackson** (1835–1911), whom his lifelong friend Sir Jonathan Hutchinson described as "the nearest to a genius that it is my privilege to have known". He was referred to affectionately as "the Sage of Manchester Square", and was in the words of Critchely "the acclaimed Master, the father of British Neurology", whilst Sir Henry Head called him "the greatest scientific clinician of the nineteenth century". A form of epilepsy is named after him. As an antidote to any excess of hero-worship, however, one of his literary eccentricities to which Critchley also refers may be mentioned: "Most of his reading consisted in yellow-backs: the shockers, thrillers and Westerns of the Victorian era." His reading technique was to tear the book in two and stuff half into each coat pocket. As each leaf was read it was discarded, and in this way he would while away the long carriage drive to and from London Hospital, a practice which did not endear him to contemporary bibliophiles.

He was originally apprenticed to an apothecary in York and studied at the Medical School there which the Apothecaries' Company had helped to promote. On April 10, 1857, he received his Diploma at the Hall, and a few months afterwards he became a member of the College of Surgeons. Later, he was elected a physician to the National Hospital in Queen Square, just two years after its foundation, and a Fellow of both the Royal Society and the Royal College of Physicians. He died honoured and mourned by his profession, leaving an unforgettable stamp upon the discipline of neurology.

There would seem to be no good reason why our interest in eminent apothecaries should be confined to those who are dead. Let us also consider briefly a couple who are happily still with us and who share the currently unique distinction of having been elected Master of the Society for two years consecutively.

Sir Charles Dodds, Bt., F.R.S., is a celebrated biochemist. At the age of 25 he was appointed as first Director of the great Courtauld Institute which had been founded at the Middlesex Hospital, and when elected as Professor by the University of London he was the youngest ever to have held a Chair. In 1938 he was able to announce his epoch-making discovery of the very powerful synthetic oestrogen compound known as Stilboestrol.

During the illness of George V he was chosen by Lord Dawson to assist him, which he did chiefly by removing large quantities of the Royal blood for analysis by the new and rapid methods he was then introducing. Soon afterwards he was elected a Fellow of the Royal College of Physicians, of which body he ultimately became President, the first Master of our Society to have achieved this position as "Head of the Profession". He was also made a Vice-President of the Royal Society in 1957, and has been the recipient of more than a dozen medical and scientific degrees and diplomas *honoris causa* from universities so far apart as Bologna and Chicago.

Dodds's pioneer interest in the science of dietetics was notable, and he once startled fellow apothecaries assembled in Hall for dinner by informing them that should they already have partaken of the usual meals that day they had already ingested 2,500 calories, sufficient to support a sedentary worker for twenty-four hours. "From a stealthy preview" of their menu he had worked out that the forthcoming meal would supply a similar calorie content, "while if beverages other than water were to be consumed at least another 800 calories must be added. In order to overcome the effects of all these," he advised, "it will be necessary to play five and a half hours' squash, or alternatively to climb a mountain the height of Ben Nevis five times, to walk sixty miles, or to run thirty miles. As another alternative, fifty hours' submersion in a cold bath would be effective." Sir Charles has recently confirmed the scientific accuracy of these remarks! Notwithstanding all this, he was an extremely popular and respected Master, and has been the Society's valued adviser on wine for many years. He is now "Father of the Court". In spite of his innate personal modesty, his name is known to students all over the world for his book *Recent Advances in Medicine* which is now in its fifteenth edition.

Our immediate Past-Master, **Sir Arthur Porritt,** Bt., was born in New Zealand and came to Magdalen College, Oxford, as a Rhodes scholar. A great athlete, he established several records in University running. His record for the 100 yards, achieved in a snowstorm, was only surpassed a year or two ago. In 1924 he was bronze medalist in the Olympic Games at Berlin. Later he became a member of the International Olympic Committee, and in 1950 he presided over the British Empire and Commonwealth Games, and was subsequently awarded the K.C.M.G.

In 1946 he was appointed Surgeon to the Royal Household, and rose to occupy the historic post of Sergeant-Surgeon to Her Majesty; for this he was appointed Knight Commander of the Royal Victorian Order. During the war he was Consulting Surgeon to Montgomery's 21st Army Group, crossing to France with the invading armies, where he was very popular owing to his cheerful optimism and easy approachability.

Porritt returned to peacetime practice as surgeon to St. Mary's Hospital, and in due course he was elected President of the Royal College of Surgeons, a position he filled with great distinction for three years. He also found time to become President of the British Medical Association, and to collect countless honorary degrees and decorations from countries all over the world, including the Fellowship of his sister College—the Physicians.

This was not to prove the culmination of his brilliant and successful life's work, however, for early in 1967 his appointment as Governor-General of New Zealand was announced, and he has returned in that exalted capacity to his native land. This is the first appointment ever to be made of a practising medical man to such a post, and the Society basks in reflected glory. It will be five years before we can welcome him back to the Apothecaries' Hall.

VIII

The
Hall
and its
Contents

OF THE THIRTY-SIX CITY LIVERY
Halls which were standing in 1939 only that of the Apothecaries survived the
war without serious damage. But it had several narrow escapes. In October
1940 a bomb hit the north end of the building and penetrated to the ground,
passing through the Parlour, but failed to explode. The result is that the
Hall and its immediate surroundings is still largely as it was rebuilt after
the Great Fire of London in 1666. It is now the veteran of the City Halls and
is also the oldest inhabited medical building in the country.

The Courtyard, which was repaved for the 350th Anniversary celebrations, is entered from Black Friars Lane through a classic doorway surmounted by the Arms of the Society. In the centre is the well which was
used by the inhabitants of the original monastery, which is now surmounted
by an elegant lamp and pedestal of Georgian design. Beyond may be seen
a pile of stones from the original Dominican establishment. The surrounding
walls are of stuccoed brick. It was on the south side that the Society's
laboratories were situated from the seventeenth until the present century.
The stone stairs in the south-east corner, which are no longer used, were
made in 1671 by Young the stonemason at his own cost to discharge a debt
incurred during the Fire of London.

In the Entrance Hall is a large monastic refectory table, which is probably the oldest object owned by the Society. Here also hangs the Armada painting referred to in the previous chapter, and a valuable long-case clock of the seventeenth century by J. Fromanteel. An attractive collection of ancient apothecaries' jars appropriately housed lines the west wall. The kitchens and offices are also on this floor.

Ascending the handsome, pine staircase with its pleasant barley-sugar balustrading and moulded handrail arranged round a well, we reach the main floor where the Great Hall, the Court Room and the Parlour stand on the old foundations of the guest-house of the friars' cloister. We are greeted by a terracotta bust of Charles I by Bernini which stands upon a fine eighteenth-century *materia medica* chest which still contains some of its original drugs. Behind us over the staircase are three large panels of ancient heraldic glass (1671), lit from behind. Turning to the right we shall find what is euphemistically named the Library, although no books now remain, and

The courtyard with the Apothecaries' shop, c. 1815.

The Court Room.

The main landing.

The Parlour.

The oak screen in the Hall above the bust of
Gideon De Laune.

its regrettable modern function is chiefly as dressing-room for waiters. Historically, however, it is of the greatest interest, as it constitutes the home portion of the bridge across the Fleet River between the Hall and the Palace of Bridewell, built in 1522 to allow Henry VIII's guest, the Holy Roman Emperor Charles V, free access from one to the other. It was across this also that the King, Catherine of Aragon, and Cardinals Wolsey and Campeggio crossed for the hearing of the Queen's trial in the Hall in Black Friars.

On the opposite side of the landing lies the entrance to the Great Hall, which is over sixty feet long and thirty wide, and was panelled in dark Irish oak wainscoting in 1671 by subscription of the members to replace the one destroyed in the Great Fire. The fine carving of the screen at the south end was done by the King's Master Carver, Henry Phillips, in the same year. On this is the bust of Gideon De Laune, already mentioned, and on either side are large contemporary portraits of James I and Charles I. The noteworthy twenty-four-branch two-tier candelabrum which hangs from the centre of the Adamesque ceiling was presented by a Past Master, Sir Benjamin Rawling, in 1737, together with an endowment for candles in perpetuity. His full-length portrait hangs opposite. It is flanked by a pair of twelve-branched French candelabra presented in 1930. At the other end of the Hall is a great chest of oriental design possibly used in the drug trade and presented by a Past Master in 1668. Above is the Minstrels' Gallery, hung with brocade which was used in Westminster Abbey at the last Coronation. The old pennants and banners which used to fly from the Society's Barge can still be seen aloft. The windows contain the armorial bearings of Past-Masters and Honorary Freemen in stained glass.

Next door is the Court Room, also splendidly panelled in 1672. On this hangs a fine portrait of James I painted on wood, together with others of Past-Masters and other eminent worthies. These include the portrait of Gideon De Laune which has been referred to in earlier chapters, while special mention must also be made of Sir Joshua Reynolds's well-known sketch of John Hunter, the celebrated surgeon, wearing a beard. It is said that his wife requested the artist to think of some way of having this removed, which he did by insisting that he must have a plaster cast made of Hunter's face. The final portrait, which hangs in the College of Surgeons, shows him without it! The ormolu candelabrum and the wall sconces date from the mid-eighteenth century. To commemorate the Charter celebrations members of the Court subscribed to

Entrance to the Hall from Black Friars Lane, 1904.

place the Society's Arms in one window and the Royal Arms in the other.

The end room is named the Parlour and contains the Society's well-known collection of antique, decorated, glazed apothecaries' jars and pill-slabs, both English and foreign, many of great beauty, in an illuminated cabinet which lines the south wall. There is also a fine pine mantel by William Kent, and double pine doors leading to the Brande Rooms and laboratory, where examinations are held; W. T. Brande, F.R.S., was the Society's Professor of Chemistry at the Hall, and became Master in 1851. A collection of miniature portraits of past and contemporary Masters is now being amassed, and hung on each side of the life-size portrait of Professor Brande, subscribed by his colleagues, which hung in the Royal Academy in 1852. There are also a number of other interesting portraits in the Parlour (see Appendix II) together with an eighteen-branch candelabrum presented by Sir Charles Dodds, and some notable eighteenth-century mahogany furniture.

On the floors above are situated the Master's quarters, the Clerk's flat, the Ancient Apothecaries' Dormitory, and a number of other rooms, which include the library of the Faculty of the History of Medicine and Pharmacy.

At one time the Society, like most City Companies, was rich in antique gold and silver plate. Of this, comparatively little remains. This is due partly to thefts, of which there are records throughout the Minutes, and also to the Act of Parliament in 1756 which decreed a heavy tax on such possessions and led the Court to sell "all such as is useless and unfashionable", including, alas, two silver-gilt "College" cups presented by Gideon De Laune himself. We do not know what happened to such interesting items as the Barge-Master's "great regalia" and the gilded crowns worn on feast-days by Master and Wardens.

The oldest pieces still in the Society's possession are the early Monteith bowl with a scalloped rim to hold the feet of the punch glasses dated 1689 which was exchanged by the Court for "old useless plate and spoons" on September 3, 1689, and the silver Salver-on-Foot, presented by the Past Master, Mr. Chase, a few days later. The fine Rosewater dish dated 1683 was probably purchased.

There are some interesting and decorative eighteenth-century pieces of which mention may be made of the set of six table candlesticks (1726) presented by John Meeres, F.R.S., Clerk to the Society, and the fine "Waiter" bought with a bequest from Mr. John Allen, the Royal Apothecary and Master (1736), the two handled loving-cup (1789) and the silver coffee-pots dated 1712. There are a considerable number of other decorative and interesting pieces of later date, mostly gifts from members of the Livery and Court, including the high silver-gilt Nuremberg Cup which usually stands in front of the Master. The eighteen-carat gold snuff-box with the Arms of the City of London in enamel presented to Edward Jenner in 1803 should be mentioned, as well as the small but interesting early-eighteenth-century Bedel's Leading-staff which precedes the procession at all official functions of the Society.

The Society's plate is normally kept at the bank for safety, but is on view at all formal dinner and other parties.

A large proportion of the furniture, pictures, hangings and plate contained in the Hall has been donated by Past Masters and members of the Society—many still living—to beautify their ancient and historic Hall. Space unfortunately does not permit detailed mention of these sources.

Envoi

OUT OF THE MISTS OF TIME EMERGE the figures of the Spicer and the Pepperer, often affluent tradesmen whose guilds were shortly to merge with that of the medieval apothecary-grocer. His increasing prosperity depended upon the import of rare drugs from newly discovered parts of the world and the compounding and dispensing of medicinal herbs already available.

In the seventeenth century the apothecaries escaped from their subservient status within the powerful City Grocers' Company and were accorded a Royal Charter as a mark of their Sovereign's personal favour. Through the next three centuries, by hard work and unflagging ambition, often against great opposition, they evolved uniquely to the status, and later to the traditions of a professional corporation, with legal power to license the practice of medicine.

Thus the Company achieved the best of both worlds. Initially as a craft guild it looked to the City of London for its rights and privileges, which included the training of its apprentices. After the Apothecaries' Act of 1815 it found itself entrusted by Parliament as supreme dictator of general medical practice with control of medical education throughout England and Wales and the legal right to qualify medical men in the same way as the two Royal

Colleges. The result was the general practitioner or family doctor of today. Thus the Society of Apothecaries is unique among City Companies, as it is in the Medical Corporations. It remains a craft guild although its particular craft has developed from a trade into a learned profession.

During those three-and-a-half centuries of continuous activity a great wealth of documents and records has accumulated of which this volume has aimed to précis what seems of most general interest.

The Society is still fulfilling its developmental intentions, stimulated by its ancient and honourable past. It faces the changing present and future with enthusiasm. Its opportunities are exceptional, for it remains the one body in England which by its constitution represents all branches of medical practice.

Whilst remaining justifiably proud of its City connections and traditions, it patriotically combines both in its sponsorship of the City of London General Hospital (T.A.). It continues to license medical practitioners as well as dispensers and to pursue its post-graduate medical courses, lectures and other activities. The full Court meets quarterly and the private Court, which consists of the Master and Wardens together with the Clerk, holds a monthly meeting after which at an informal dinner it entertains half a dozen post-graduate students from the Commonwealth—a pleasant and unusual custom.

The Society's lovely and historic home was the only City Hall completely to survive the wartime bombing of London, and so remains the oldest existing in its entirety, and indeed the oldest medical building in this country.

The 350th Anniversary of the Granting of the Society's Charter has not passed unnoticed by the outside world. It was celebrated by a solemn service in St. Paul's Cathedral which was attended by the Lord Mayor, Sheriffs and the Corporation of the City of London. On December 6, 1967, which was the anniversary date of the award, H.M. The Queen Mother honoured the Livery by attendance at their banquet and graciously accepted a copy of this book; whilst congratulations were received from the highest in the land, amongst others ex-Premier Harold Macmillan, the Archbishop of Canterbury, the Duke of Norfolk (Earl Marshal of England), the Lord Chief Justice and his Judges, and the Minister of Health, all of whom dined in the Great Hall. The Heads of all the other Medical Corporations and Royal Colleges together with the President of the Royal Society visited in state, whilst the Freedom of the Society *Honoris Causa* was conferred upon the

Chancellors of the Universities of Oxford and Cambridge. The Society's learned Clerk was made an Honorary Licentiate (a very unusual honour), whilst the Honorary Secretary of the Faculty of the History of Medicine and Pharmacy, Dr. F. N. L. Poynter, had the Freedom of the Society conferred.

The History of the Worshipful Society of Apothecaries which is briefly told in this volume has been the major influence in moulding the structure of medical practice as we know it today in this country. The special relevance of its earlier achievements—often against tenacious opposition—to those changes in the way in which medical knowledge and traditions are now being applied to education and to the service of the community, which resulted from the establishment of the National Health Service in 1948, has been of the greatest significance to practitioners of Medicine, and in a special sense their patients who after all are the *raison d'être* for the Society's continuing existence.

Let us end with the pious aspiration which is pleasantly reflected in the Master's Toast given at all dinners: "The Worshipful Society of Apothecaries of London; may it flourish root and branch bringing help and health to all, till time ceases."

The Society's Coat of Arms.

The Appendices

APPENDIX I

Roll of Past Masters

DATE	MASTER	DATE	MASTER
1618	*Edmund Phillips	1636–37	*John Wolfgang Rumler (John Wolfe)
1618–19	,, ,,		
1619–20	,, ,,	1637–38	*Gideon De Laune
1620–21	,, ,,	1638–39	*Stephen Higgins
1621–22	*Stephen Higgins	1639–40	*Edward Cooke
1622–23	*John Wolfgang Rumler	1640–41	,, ,,
1623–24	*Richard Bacon	1641–42	*William Bell
1624–25	*Thomas Fones	1642–43	*Ralph Yardley
1625–26	,, ,,	1643–44	*Abraham Webb
1626–27	*Adrian Barton	1644–45	*William Shambrook
1627–28	*Josias Harryes	1645–46	*Richard Glover
1628–29	*Gideon De Laune	1646–47	John Sotherton
1629–30	*Israel Wolfe	1647–48	John Lawrence
1630–31	*Thomas Christie	1648–49	Oliver Reynolds
1632–32	*William Clapham	1649–50	*James Walsham
1632–33	*Richard Edwards	1650–51	Samuel Harrison
1633–34	,, ,,	1651–52	Samuel Skelton
1634–35	*Thomas Hicks	1652–53	Richard Holland
1635–36	*Josias Harris (Harryes)	1653–54	Thomas Smith

* Original Member.

DATE	MASTER	DATE	MASTER
1654–55	John Lorymer (Senr.)	1686–87	William Pott
1655–56	James James	1687–88	James St. Amand, M.P.
1656–57	Leonard Buckner	1688–89	James Chase
	James Martin	1689–90	Thomas Warren
1657–58	John Thomas	1690–91	James Gover
1658–59	Caleb Stephens	1691–92	William Bradford
1659–60	Richard Markland	1692–93	Thomas Hall ⎫
	(?Michael)		Thomas Soaper ⎭
1660–61	John Shelburie	1693–94	Henry Sykes
1661–62	William Rousewell	1694–95	Sir John Clarke
1662–63	Jeremiah Richardson	1695–96	John Danson
1663–64	Benjamin Banister	1696–97	Thomas Fige
1664–65	John Chase	1697–98	William Phillipps
1665–66	,, ,,	1698–99	Spencer Piggott ⎫
1667–67	Michael North		Thomas Elton ⎭
1667–68	Edward Darnelly	1699–00	Thomas Elton
1668–69	Richard Litlar	1700–01	Thomas Dalton
1669–70	Symon Williams	1701–02	Peter Gelsthorp
1670–71	Arthur Hollingsworth	1702–03	Thomas Gardiner
1671–72	Walter Pelling	1703–04	Peter Gelsthorp
1672–73	William Gape	1704–05	Arthur Reeves
1673–74	George Johnson	1705–06	William Rouse
1674–75	John Battersby	1706–07	Thomas Bromfield
1675–76	Anthony Hinton	1707–08	Richard Malther
1676–77	Edward Pilkington	1708–09	Francis Danbridge
1677–78	William Butler	1709–10	,, ,,
1678–79	Thomas Warner	1710–11	Walter Drewry
1679–80	Thomas Mitchell	1711–12	Joseph Biscoe
1680–81	Stephen Skynner ⎫	1712–13	Jonathan Lee
	Robert Phelps ⎭	1713–14	Thomas Compere
1681–82	William Standen	1714–15	Samuel Birch
1682–83	William Clerke	1715–16	John Jay
1683–84	Peter Sambrooke	1716–17	Simon Andrews
1684–85	†Thomas Barrow	1717–18	Henry Smith
		1718–19	Thomas Shaller
	New Charter	1719–20	Colonel Robert Gower
1685–86	Edward Herne ⎫	1720–21	James Siddall
	Benjamin Donne ⎭	1721–22	Joseph Nicholson

† Did not take office, Sambrooke continued to act until 26 February, 1685, when the New Charter was received.

DATE	MASTER		DATE	MASTER	
1722–23	Joseph Nicholson ⎫		1758–59	Andrew Lillie ⎫	
	Henry Smith ⎭			William Tyson ⎭	
1723–24	James Pitson		1759–60	William Gataker	
1724–25	Oliver Gaynes		1760–61	Benjamin Charlewood	
1725–26	Simon Andrews		1761–62	Daniel Hanchett	
1726–27	Colonel Robert Gower		1762–63	John Springett	
1727–28	John Smith		1763–64	Josiah Higden	
1728–29	Charles Angebaud		1764–65	Sir Thomas Harris	
1729–30	John Bicoes		1765–66	Benjamin Charlewood ⎫	
1730–31	Josiah Cruttenden			Edmund Mills ⎭	
1731–32	William Withers		1766–67	John Peck	
1732–33	Ralph Forster		1767–68	Marmaduke Westwood ⎫	
1733–34	John Warren			John Chandler, F.R.S. ⎭	
1734–35	James Albin		1768–69	Samuel Latham	
1735–36	Zachary Allen ⎫		1769–70	Jeremiah Armiger	
	Robert Hume ⎭		1770–71	John Lisle	
1736–37	Sir Benjamin Rawling		1771–72	John Channing	
1737–38	Robert Harris		1772–73	John Pearce	
1738–39	Joseph Miller		1773–74	James Kettilby	
1739–40	John Salter		1774–75	Josiah Colebrooke, F.R.S. ⎫	
1740–41	Robert Nicholls			Thomas Basden ⎭	
1741–42	Benjamin Morris		1775–76	William Prowting	
1742–43	Joseph Richards		1776–77	George Clarke	
1743–44	John Lyde		1777–78	William Lane	
1744–45	Robert Gamon		1778–79	Thomas Roberts	
1745–46	John de Raffen		1779–80	Richard Elliott	
1746–47	William Lake		1780–81	Joseph Partington	
1747–48	John Pocklington		1781–82	Isaac Mather	
1748–49	Nathaniel Green		1782–83	Thomas Hawes	
1749–50	Reuben Melmoth		1783–84	Edward Thomas Nealson	
1750–51	William Elderton		1784–85	John Devall	
1751–52	John Addis		1785–86	John Field	
1752–53	Thomas Northey ⎫		1786–87	Matthew Yatman	
	Robert Gamon ⎭		1787–88	James Bromfield	
1753–54	John Chase		1788–89	Peter Girod	
1754–55	John Markham		1789–90	Thomas Cater	
1755–56	Samuel Berkley		1790–91	Paul Julliott	
1756–57	William Massa ⎫		1791–92	Herbert Lawrence	
	Nathaniel Greene ⎬		1792–93	William Heckford	
	Sir Benjamin Rawling ⎭		1793–94	John Willey	
1757–58	Daniel Peters		1794–95	John William Benson	

DATE	MASTER	DATE	MASTER
1795–96	John Devaynes	1836–37	John Hingeston
1796–97	William Fowle	1837–38	George Johnson
1797–98	John Bradney	1838–39	David Clapton
1798–99	Isaac Bouquet	1839–40	James Seaton ⎱
1799–00	Thomas Watson		Allen Williams ⎰
1800–01	John Collier	1840–41	Allen Williams
1801–02	Timothy Lane, F.R.S.	1841–42	Henry Robinson
1802–03	Richard Haworth	1842–43	Charles Edward Clarke
1803–04	Uriah Bristow	1843–44	William Bagster
1804–05	Augustine Towson	1844–45	Edward Wallace
1805–06	Adam Moore	1845–46	John Bacot
1806–07	Robert Sherson	1846–47	John Ridout
1807–08	Hugh French	1847–48	Edward Bean
1808–09	Elias de Gruchy Fassett	1848–49	John Callander
1809–10	William Henry Higden	1849–50	John Brown Eyles
1810–11	Charles Nevinson	1850–51	Michael Lambton Este
1811–12	Richard Griffith	1851–52	William Thomas Brande, F.R.S.
1812–13	Philip Nicholas	1852–53	Richard Strong Eyles
1813–14	John Stephen Bacot	1853–54	John Parrott
1814–15	John Newsom	1854–55	Nathaniel Bagshawe Ward, F.R.S.
1815–16	Thomas Hardwick		
1816–17	William Simons	1855–56	Richard Clewin Griffith
1817–18	William Box	1856–57	John Francis De Grave
1818–19	Miles Partington	1857–58	Jeronimo Simoens
1819–20	Samuel Lawford	1858–59	James Saner
1820–21	Joseph Jackson	1859–60	Frederick Richard Gowar
1821–22	George Cabbell	1860–61	John Hunter
1822–23	John Baker	1861–62	William Buchanan
1823–24	Thomas Wheeler	1862–63	Charles West Wheeler
1824–25	Edward Browne	1863–64	Henry Combe
1825–26	Henry Field	1864–65	James Lowe Wheeler
1826–27	Joseph Littlefear	1865–66	Charles Higham
1827–28	Juliam Mariner	1866–67	George Cooper
1828–29	Andrew Ewbank	1867–68	,, ,,
1829–30	Joseph Hurlock	1868–69	Tobias Browne
1830–31	William R. Macdonald	1869–70	Joseph Smith
1831–32	John Hunter	1870–71	Henry Morley
1832–33	James Hill	1871–72	George Kelson
1833–34	John Nussey	1872–73	Thomas Hunt
1834–35	James Upton	1873–74	William Dickinson
1835–36	William King	1874–75	Richard Stocker

98

DATE	MASTER	DATE	MASTER
1875–76	Allin Foord Price	1914–15	Meredith Townsend
1876–77	Edward Bradford	1915–16	George Amsden
1877–78	Willington Clark	1916–17	Arthur Henry Williams Ayling
1878–79	Thomas George Slaughter	1917–18	Charles Sangster
1879–80	John Hainworth	1918–19	Benjamin Bloomfield Connolly
1880–81	Thomas Spry Byass	1919–20	Samuel Osborn
1881–82	Hugh Worthington Statham	1920–21	Sir Shirley Murphy
1882–83	James Saner	1921–22	William Frederick Richardson
1883–84	Thomas Wakefield		Burgess
1884–85	George Corfe	1922–23	William Budd Slaughter
1886–86	Edward Furley	1923–24	Thomas Wakefield
1886–87	William Shillito	1924–25	Algernon Dutton Brenchley
1887–88	George John Amsden	1925–26	Thomas Vincent Dickinson
1888–89	Thomas Skeel	1926–27	Alfred Hepburn
1889–90	George Hogarth Makins	1927–28	Reginald Whiteside Statham
1890–91	Edwin Chabot	2928–29	Charles Thomas Samman
1891–92	Joyn Wadham Robinson	1929–30	,, ,,
1892–93	Charles Taylor	1930–31	,, ,,
1893–94	John Rees Withcombe	1931–32	Ernest Carrick Freeman
1894–95	Thomas James Austin	1932–33	Reginald Cecil Bligh Wall
1895–96	Francis Richard Gibbas	1933–34	John Oglethorpe Wakelin
1896–97	Edward Tegart		Barratt
1897–98	Samuel Clewin Griffith (Junr.)	1934–35	Sir George Seaton Buchanan
1898–99	Joseph Stewart Burton	1935–36	Sir William Henry Willcox
1899–00	John Sherwood Stocker	1936–37	Arthur Philip Gibbons
1900–01	Charles Browne	1937–38	Sir Hugh Lett, Bt.
1901–02	Thomas Edwin Burton Brown	1938–39	Reginald Hewlett Hayes
1902–03	William Parson	1939–40	Lionel Vernon Cargill
1903–04	Clarence Cooper	1940–41	Thomas Bramley Layton
1904–05	Albert Bryan Day	1941–42	Sir Stanley Woodwark
1905–06	James Henry Jeffcoat	1942–43	,, ,,
1906–07	Edward Parker Young	1943–44	,, ,,
1907–08	George Wilks	1944–45	John Prescott Hedley
1908–09	Frederick Gordon Brown	1945–46	Hugh Falkenberg Powell
1909–10	Reginald Bligh Wall	1946–47	Christopher Thackray Parsons
1910–11	Arthur Trehern Norton	1947–48	Sir Edward Charles Dodds, Bt.,
1911–12	Sir Thomas Boor Crosby,		F.R.S.
	Lord Mayor	1948–49	,, ,,
	Arthur Long (Deputy)	1949–50	Duncan Campbell Lloyd
1912–13	William Bramley Taylor		Fitzwilliams
1913–14	Martindale Ward	1950–51	Frank Dutch Howitt

99

DATE	MASTER	DATE	MASTER
1951–52	Gerald Roche Lynch	1960–61	Charles Francis White
1952–53	Sir Wilson Jameson	1961–62	Archie Murrell Acheson Moore
1953–54	Henry Seaward Morley	1962–63	Thomas Keith Slefe Lyle
1954–55	Sir Cecil Pembrey Gray Wakeley, Bt.	1963–64	Redvers Nowell Ironside
		1964–65	Sir Arthur Porritt, Bt.
1955–56	Neville Samuel Finzi	1965–66	Richard Alan Brews (died on Christmas Day)
1956–57	Macdonald Critchley		
1957–58	Reginald Fisher	1965–66	Sir Arthur Porritt, Bt. (for remainder of Mr. Brews's term)
1958–59	William Sydney Charles Copeman		
1959–60	Richard Robertson Trail	1966–67	Harold Clifford Edwards

Honorary Freemen

1936 Sir Arthur Salusbury MacNalty, K.C.B., M.D., F.R.C.P., F.R.C.S.

1949 Sir Charles Robert Harington, K.B.E., M.A., ph.D., F.R.S.

1951 Sir Henry Hallett Dale, O.M., G.B.E., F.R.C.P., F.R.S.

1954 Sir John Nigel Loring, K.C.V.O., M.R.C.S., L.R.C.P.

1956 Sir James Paterson Ross, Bt., K.C.V.O., M.S., F.R.C.S

1959 H.R.H. the Duke of Gloucester, F.R.S.

1962 Sir Zachary Cope, M.D., F.R.C.S.

1964 Sir Geoffrey Keynes, M.D., F.R.C.P., F.R.C.S., F.R.C.O.G.

1966 Sir Paul Chambers, K.B.E., C.B., C.I.E.

Honorary Diplomates

1962 H.R.H. The Duke of Windsor

1967 Ernest Busby

Freedom by Gift

1967 F. Noel Poynter, ph.D., F.L.A.

Court of Assistants, 1967-8

Master

Sinclair, HUGH MACDONALD, D.M., F.R.C.P., L.M.S.S.A., Magdalen College, Oxford.

Wardens

Thompson, HENRY REYNOLDS, M.B., B.Ch., F.R.C.S.
Bishop, PETER MAXWELL FARROW, D.M., F.R.C.P.

Assistants

Dodds, PROFESSOR SIR EDWARD CHARLES, Bt., M.V.O., M.D., D.SC., F.R.C.P., F.R.S.
Wakeley, SIR CECIL PEMBURY GREY, Bt., K.B.E., C.B., LL.D., D.SC., F.R.C.S.
Critchley, MACDONALD, C.B.E., M.D., F.A.C.P., F.R.C.P.
Copeman, WILLIAM SYDNEY CHARLES, C.B.E., T.D., M.A., M.D., F.R.C.P.
Trail, RICHARD ROBERTSON, C.B.E., M.C., M.A., M.D., F.R.C.P.
Moore, ARCHIE MURRELL ACHESON, F.R.C.S.
Lyle, THOMAS KEITH SELFE, C.B.E., M.A., M.D., F.R.C.P., F.R.C.S.
Ironside, REDVERS NOWELL, M.B., Ch.B., F.R.C.P.
Porritt, SIR ARTHUR ESPIE, Bt., G.C.M.G., K.C.V.O., C.B.E., M.A., F.R.C.S.
Edwards, HAROLD CLIFFORD, C.B.E., M.S., F.R.C.S.

Cashell, GEOFFREY THOMAS WILLOUGHBY, M.B., L.M.S.S.A., F.R.C.S.
Richardson, SIR JOHN SAMUEL, Bt., M.V.O., M.D., F.R.C.P.
Gunn, ALASTAIR LIVINGSTONE, V.R.D., M.D., F.R.C.S., F.R.C.O.G.
Windeyer, SIR BRIAN WELLINGHAM, M.B., B.S., F.R.C.P., F.R.C.S.
Mitchell-Heggs, GORDON BARRETT, O.B.E., T.D., F.R.C.P.
Scott, SIR RONALD BODLEY, K.C.V.O., D.M., F.R.C.P.
Davies, HUGH WILLIAM, T.D., D.M., F.F.R. (died 1967)*
Muir, EDWARD GRAINGER, M.S., F.R.C.S.
Grey-Turner, ELSTON GREY, M.C., T.D., M.A., M.R.C.S.
Teare, ROBERT DONALD, M.D., F.R.C.P., F.C.Path., D.M.J.
Jackson, IAN MACGILCHRIST, M.B., B.Chir., F.R.C.S., F.R.C.O.G.

* Rosenheim, Sir Max, K.B.E., M.D., P.R.C.P., elected in his place (1967).

A List of Pictures hanging in the Hall, December 1967

In the Entrance Hall

Queen Elizabeth reviewing her Navy after the defeat of the Spanish Armada attributed to Nicholas Hilliard (the miniaturist) 1588.

On the Staircase

The Entry of William of Orange into Exeter after landing at Torbay (1689), presented by Reuben Melmoth, Master 1749.

Thomas Hardwick, Master in the year in which Apothecaries' Act was passed (1815).

Professor Henry Morley, by Ida Morley. Warden 1892–4.

On the Landing

Queen Anne, presented by Henry Prude.

Queen Victoria, presented by Arthur Ellis to commemorate the Jubilee (1897).

King William II and Queen Mary II, presented by John Lisle, Master 1770.

The Magdalen, by Guido Reni (1575–1642), presented by Dr. S. Monckton Copeman, F.R.S. on becoming a Liveryman.

Sir Hugh Lett, Bt., P.R.C.S., by Sir James Gunn. Master 1937.

Sir Cecil Wakeley, Bt., P.R.C.S., by Frank Salisbury. Master 1954.

In the Great Hall

Isaac Rand, F.R.S., Director of the Chelsea Physic Garden.

Sir John Clarke, Sheriff of London, and Master 1694 (as Nominee of King James II).

John Brownell (Liveryman), presented by himself in 1733.

John Lorrymer (or Lorrimer), Master 1654 and benefactor.

Henry Smith, Master 1723.

King Charles I—copy after Van Dyke (1676).

King James I, by Snelling (after Van Somer). He granted the Society's Royal Charter in 1617.

Sir Benjamin Rawling, by J. Whood. Sheriff of London. Master 1736.

Henry Prude, by Thomas Hudson (who was Master to Sir Joshua Reynolds).

Colonel Robert Gower, Master 1719 and 1726.

Peter Guelsthorp, Master 1701.

William Prowting, by Lemuel Abbott; Master 1775.

John Hunter, Master 1831. No relation to the Anatomist. Member of first Court of Examiners (1815).

Banners and pennants from the Society's last State Barge (1805).

In the Court Room

Henry Field, by H. W. Pickersgill, R.A. Master 1825.

William Prowting, by L. Abbott. Master 1775 (similar to one in Great Hall).

Thomas Wheeler, F.R.S. by Henry Briggs, R.A. Master 1823—was Society's Professor of Botany, and member of the first Court of Examiners in 1815.

Samuel Dale (1659–1739), the Society's lecturer on *materia medica* and author of *Pharmacologia*. His demonstration chest is on the landing.

Marmaduke Westwood, Master 1767.

King James 1—Contemporary panel, attributed to J. de Critz, Sergeant-Painter to His Majesty.

John Hunter, the Anatomist (1728–93), by Sir Joshua Reynolds, P.R.A. This was the preliminary sketch for the famous portrait at the R.C.S. Mrs. Hunter disliked the final portrait on account of the beard and gave it to James Weatherall. The sketch was presented to the Society by his nephew Thomas Knight, Liveryman.

George Johnson, by Sir Godfrey Kneller. Master 1673.

Mary Queen of Scots (miniature) presented by Edward Hollier, Liveryman. Also a miniature portrait believed to represent Anne of Denmark, Consort to King James I.

Cornelius Dutch, by Thomas Hudson. "Faithful Clerk to the Society for 30 years."

John Allen, by Thomas Hudson. Master, Apothecary to the Royal Household, and benefactor.

Gideon De Laune, at 76, attributed to Cornelius Janssen (1640). Founder of the Society and Master 1628 and 1637. Apothecary to Anne of Denmark, Consort to King James I.

Dr. Richard Mead, F.R.C.P. (1673–1748). Inaugurated coffee-house consultations with Apothecaries.

John Markham, Master 1754. Apothecary to the Charterhouse.

Dr. George Mann Burrows, F.R.C.P. Largely responsible for the Apothecaries' Act of 1815; portrait commissioned by the Society "in gratitude".

Josiah Higden, by Thomas Hudson. Master 1763.

Richard Clewin Griffith, by A. E. Fisher. Master 1855.

Inscribed panel from stern of the Society's State Barge (1690).

In the Parlour

Reginald Bligh Wall, by Collier Smithers. Master 1909. Presented by his son Dr. R. C. B. Wall who was Master in 1932.

Nathaniel Bagshaw Ward, F.R.S., by J. P. Knight, R.A. Master 1854. He invented the "Wardian Case" whereby the tea industry of India was started.

William Thomas Brande, F.R.S., by H. Weigall. Master 1851. Was Society's Professor of Chemistry and *Materia Medica*. An educational reformer.

Lt. Col. Charles Samman, J.P., by F. W. Elwell, A.R.A. Master 1928–31. In this picture can be seen some of the Society's interesting possessions and plate.

Duncan C. L. Fitzwilliams, C.M.G., F.R.C.S., by Maurice Codner, A.R.A. Master 1949.

Index